# CLARKSTON'S CURSE

# CLARKSTON'S CURSE

One Child's Quest to Explain the Series of
Tragedies in Her Hometown

Ann Margaret Johns

P.O. Box 1495

Clarkston MI 48347-1495

annmargaretauthor@gmail.com

Published 2017

Printed in the United States of America

ISBN: 978-0-9993457-0-2

eBook ISBN: 978-0-9993457-1-9

*This book is dedicated to the family and friends of those whose lives were lost due to the tragedies written about in this book. When others tell you "time will heal your pain," I know, like you, that time doesn't heal the pain, it just dulls it a bit.*

*In loving memory of Nancy Rekawek,*

*Fly like an Eagle—Steve Miller Band*

# Contents

# Foreword

The inspiration for this book came while dining in a Chinese restaurant near the Michigan Technological University campus with my eldest daughter during her senior year in college. My fortune cookie message read, You must write your words. Just the week prior, my childhood friend Sue had suggested I write a book. And so, I did.

Thanks to Mom for always believing in me; to my youngest daughter, Janet Marie, whose love and support through so many trying years has been invaluable; to my oldest daughter, Kathryn, whose amazing journey helped me get here. And to my editor, Cristen Iris, I am looking forward to working with you on the next chapter.

# Introduction

Kathryn once told me that our minds are like filing cabinets. We have file folders we put our memories in, and then we take out a folder when needed. I put my childhood memories in a file folder and shut the drawer. Until now. I hope you find this book engaging and entertaining. A few names were changed to protect people's privacy, but every word on these pages was written exactly as I remember.

# One
# File Folders

"Annie, come in here," my father, Clancy, hollered through the back-porch window. The day was warm, but not too warm, like some days can get in summertime in Michigan. I'd placed my dolls in a circle on a blanket and we'd been enjoying an imaginary cup of tea. Mom had just finished mowing the lawn. The smell of fresh-cut grass hung in the air. A slight breeze cooled my skin. The year was 1969.

"Hurry up girl; history is about to be made."

I had no idea what "history" was, but based on Dad's sense of urgency, I figured it must be important. The wooden porch door slammed behind me as I ran toward the couch and jumped down right next to him.

"You are about to see man step on the moon for the first time, Annie."

My father's breath had the faint, familiar aroma of scotch as he spoke. I studied his handsome face. His hair was thick and black. Wide, dark sideburns framed the sides of my father's cheekbones. His eyes were green, turned slightly downward under thick black eyebrows. I turned my attention to the small black and white television set.

Neil Armstrong was the first astronaut to exit the spaceship. Once outside, he lowered a small ladder that held a camera so my family and I, and millions of other people, could watch "history." Armstrong touched the moon's surface and said, "That's one small step for man, one giant leap for mankind." My mother was pregnant at the time.

It seemed to me that my mother was pregnant every summer while we lived in Berkley, Michigan, but in actuality, she was only pregnant five times. The first two pregnancies created my brother Patrick and me. The third and fourth ended in miscarriages. With each miscarriage, Mom would go to the hospital where she would stay for a few days. Dad would stay home and hit the scotch for a few days. When Mom returned home from the hospital, she would be sad and distant. Our father treated her as though the miscarriages were somehow her fault. He felt it was a woman's duty to produce many sons. Bless my mother's heart. She tried.

A year had passed since Mom's second miscarriage. She was pregnant for the fifth time. This pregnancy was almost full term, and I was extremely optimistic that she was going to have a baby this time.

"How much longer until the baby comes?" I asked. I had my small hand on her big belly hoping to feel the baby kick.

"Not much longer now," Mom said with a smile.

Smiling back, I studied my mother's face. She was beautiful. Not the kind of beautiful that makes you stop in your tracks but the kind of beautiful that takes you by surprise. Everything from her jet-black hair to her sparkling blue eyes was beautiful. From her mind to her bones. My mother's beauty radiated off her. She embodies the same kind of beauty my grandmother had, the same kind of beauty I hoped I might one day have.

Grandma told me Mom needed lots of rest. The more time she spent off her feet the better it was for the baby. I did my best to be a good helper. Looking back, I am sure my constant doting drove her nuts.

As young as I was, I could see the strain on her face and realized the toll it took on my poor pregnant mother to get us dressed and to church on time. I think she was just as happy as my brother and I were to finally be home from Mass.

"Please go find your brother. Tell him to change into his play clothes and get outside. You change out of that dress too."

"Okay, Mom," I said skipping through the small dining room toward the attic stairway.

Patrick's bedroom was in the attic of our house. The stairs were steep, so I used the handrail to help propel myself up. I found my brother sitting on the floor playing with his G.I. Joes. "Mom wants you to play outside. She sent me to fetch you. Told me to tell you to change out of your church clothes and get outdoors."

Patrick ignored me as he moved tanks around the floor and made war noises. I stood there for a few moments watching him, waiting for a response. My brother was the spitting image of our mother. Patrick inherited her dark wavy hair and striking blue eyes. He had just gotten all his adult teeth in. I thought his teeth looked too big for his face. Mom said his face would catch up.

I wasn't about to hang around for his response. I grabbed the handrail and bounced back down the stairs, heading toward my bedroom to change my clothes then outside to see if any girls were outdoors ready to play.

"One, two, three," I counted, hands covering my eyes, my body leaning into a big tree. Some girls who lived a few doors down had invited me to play a game of hide-and-go-seek. I finished counting at number ten, uncovered my eyes, and began looking around for the other children. I didn't spot any of the girls, but I did spot Grandma's big Oldsmobile 98 pulling into our driveway. My grandparents never came out to the city on a Sunday, so I was certain Grandma was here because it was time for Mom to have the baby. I ditched on the game of hide-and-go-seek and ran home as fast I could.

I caught up to Grandma just as her hand was reaching for the back storm door. I slapped my hands on my knees, catching my breath.

"Is the baby coming?" I gasped.

She looked at me lovingly but didn't speak.

"Well? Is the baby coming?" I looked up and asked again.

Grandma started to smile sweetly. Not her usual happy smile but a cautious smile. More guarded I would say. I could tell she was choosing her words carefully. *Oh God, please, not again,* I thought. I was so excited to have a baby brother or sister. *Mom will be devastated if she loses another baby. I'll be devastated if she loses another baby.* Before Grandma had a chance to answer my question, Dad stumbled out of the house and onto the stoop. He didn't say a word to either one of us. His attention focused on Mom as he tried to assist her down the two concrete steps to the driveway. Dad was clearly "in the sauce" as Grandma would say.

"No baby today, Annie," Grandma finally responded. "Your mother tripped on the stairs and twisted her ankle real bad. She needs to go to the hospital to make sure she didn't break it." Grandma was glaring at Dad. I could tell she was spitting nails mad.

"The baby is fine, Annie. Don't worry," she said ruffling the hair on the top of my head.

Grandma and I stood there on the stoop watching Dad as he tried to help Mom into the car.

"For God's sake Clancy, watch my good foot!"

"I'm just trying to help you, Patsy!" Dad pushed Mom's right leg into the car and slammed the door shut. He staggered to the driver's side of the car and opened the door.

"Are you sure I shouldn't drive to the hospital, Clancy? I don't think you are in any shape to drive."

"I've got it, Ruth!"

Dad almost took out the mailbox backing out of the driveway. Once his car was out of sight, Grandma and I took worry-filled steps into the house.

Miniature pieces of wood furniture were scattered about my bedroom floor. I was contemplating how I should place them back into the dollhouse when I heard a soft knock on the door. I didn't respond. The door open slightly. Grandma's sweet face peeked into my room.

"Are you hungry, dear?"

"Not really," I replied, not looking up, focused on the task at hand. Grandma sat down on the floor next to me. She picked up a couch and set it down gently in the middle room on the second floor. I picked up a coffee table, leaned close to her, and placed the table in front of the couch. I breathed in the sweet smell of my grandma. I loved the way Grandma smelled, a mix of White Shoulders, fresh lake air, and love.

"Will you help me bake a pie? I saw some apples in the kitchen."

I looked up at her light-blue, twinkling eyes and smiled. "Sure Grandma, I'll help you."

Standing up, Grandma reached for my hand. I put my hand in hers, and she pulled me up off the floor. Her hand was almost as small as mine. Her skin was soft. I ran my fingers gently over the veins that protruded from under her skin.

"Do they hurt?" I asked.

"No, they don't hurt," she laughed.

Grandma was short, not much taller than me really. She grabbed the step stool out of the corner so she could reach the cupboard where Mom kept the pie tins.

"Can you get the apples for me?"

"Sure!"

As I retrieved the apples, Grandma tossed flour, Crisco, and water into a glass pie tin. She mixed the three ingredients with her fingers until they became a ball of dough. She sprinkled some flour onto the kitchen counter, tossed the dough ball onto the flour, and quickly rolled out a thin crust. She tossed the crust into the pie tin. The entire process took her just a few minutes. It was like watching a magician.

Grandma and I were enjoying a piece of our pie with a side of vanilla ice cream when Mom and Dad returned from the hospital. Thankfully, Mom was still very much pregnant, but now with her foot in a cast. The combination of her big belly and the cast on her foot made her ill equipped to care for two small children. Grandma visited as often as she could helping with housework and fixing meals. Grandpa was not pleased that Grandma was spending so much time in the city. He thought it was Dad's place to take care of his wife. Dad said he had a business to run, so he didn't have time to stay home playing nursemaid to our mother. It was obvious to me that my mom felt guilty having to depend on her mother. Grandpa depended on Grandma to help him run his small business, and it made Mom feel bad that Grandma had to help care for us.

My grandpa had his own business making dentures, crowns, and bridges for local dentists. His laboratory, or "lab" as he called it, was on Sashabaw Road right next to the Dream Twist ice cream parlor. I loved to visit Grandpa's lab. He used mercury in some of the dental stuff he made. Hard to believe today, but he would let me pour the liquid metal out on his desk, and I would actually pick it up and try to hold it. Grandpa had a magnet in his desk drawer. I would push the mercury around with the magnet. He also had lead, and he would let me help melt and pour it into molds to make weights for his fishing lures.

Sometimes Grandpa gave me twenty-five cents so I could run next door to the Dream Twist and get an ice cream cone. Grandma's job was to deliver the dental fixtures to the local dentists' offices. Delivery days were Tuesdays and Thursdays. Mom was on her own those days.

On Tuesdays and Thursdays, Mom did her best to manage. Exhaustion would set in just from the effort of trying to balance on one leg to make breakfast. Lucky for her, it was summertime. She sent my brother and me outside to play, which kept us out of her way. Patrick usually played catch or kick ball with the neighbor boys. I sometimes played with the neighbor girls, but mostly I played by myself with my trusty dolls.

Mrs. Beasley was by far my favorite. Square glasses sat atop her tiny, slightly turned-up nose. I loved her rosy cheeks, bright blue eyes, and friendly smile. She always wore the same blue, polka dot dress and a small ribbon in her short blond hair. Mrs. Beasley and I were enjoying a tea party on the front lawn when my brother had his first run in with the law.

"Would you like some more tea, Mrs. Beasley?" I asked as I pulled the string on her left hip. She responded, "I do think you're the nicest little friend I ever had."

"Well, thank you, Mrs. Beasley. I think you're the nicest friend I've ever had too."

After pouring a little tea (milk) into Mrs. Beasley's teacup, I reached into the picnic basket and took out two small plastic plates. After daintily placing the white plates down on the blanket, I reached back into our basket for two chocolate chip cookies. I set one cookie on Mrs. Beasley's plate and took a bite of the other. As I was savoring the delicious tastes of chocolate and brown sugar, I noticed a police car slowly cruising down our street.

As one would expect, the police officer had the car window rolled down with his arm bent in the open space, the fingers of his hand holding onto the roof. The officer looked out the cruiser window in my direction. Sunglasses hit his eyes. He smiled and waved at me. I waved back as he passed our small house. Out of nowhere, Patrick appeared in the front yard. "Pig!" he screamed.

The officer stopped the patrol car, backed up, and pulled in our driveway. Patrick took off running. He jumped the backyard fence and jetted across the neighbor's yard. He was long gone by the time the police officer got out of his patrol car.

"This isn't good," I said to Mrs. Beasley.

The patrol car radio squawked something I couldn't make out. The officer spoke back into his radio. I couldn't quite hear what he said. He got out of his car. With his hands in his pockets, he slowly strolled up the driveway. He stopped and stood just a foot away. His large frame blocked the sun and cast a shadow over Mrs. Beasley and me.

The officer slowly took off his sunglasses. He had dark, serious eyes. "Is your mother home, little miss?" he asked.

I tried to respond, but I couldn't find my voice. My heart was racing. My palms started to sweat. I grabbed Mrs. Beasley and pulled her tight against my chest. I finally found the courage to speak.

"Yes, sir," I answered my voice barely audible.

The police officer turned and walked up the front porch steps. He rang the doorbell. His head turned from side to side surveying the neighborhood as he waited for my mother to come and open the door. But Mom didn't come to the door. I was sure she was ignoring it, thinking it was Patrick or me. The police officer rang the bell again. Moments ticked by like hours. The police officer pushed the bell a third time. Suddenly and forcefully, the front storm door flew open. So suddenly it startled the police officer. I could see Mom's crutch. Then I saw her big, fat, pregnant belly followed by her foot in the cast. Out next came a second crutch.

Finally, Mom's huge body was on the front stoop. Leaning on her crutches, she wore her *angry face.*

Trust me. No one ever wants to see my mother's angry face. I swear, those blue, Irish eyes can shoot sparks and burn holes right through your skin. The look on the police officer's face when his eyes met hers was priceless. I didn't think police officers were scared of anything, but it was pretty clear this one was scared of my mom. The officer took his hat off and tipped it to her. "I see you have your hands full here ma'am. Have a nice day."

I watched the officer swiftly return to his cruiser. He didn't look in my direction as he walked back to his police car, got inside it, and left. Patrick wouldn't be going to jail. At least not that day.

Summer was winding down, and the baby was due to arrive any day. With her foot finally out of its cast, Mom could focus on making a room for the baby. She chose to use my bedroom as a nursery. I was not thrilled when my parents broke the news that they were moving my bedroom into the attic where my brother's room was. In an attempt to make two separate bedroom spaces for us, Mom had sewn a curtain divider. She had Dad install it, separating the attic space into two smaller spaces. I was not the least bit happy about having to share a room with my brother, but was overjoyed about the new baby.

Mom did a wonderful job decorating the nursery. My old room looked as if it had popped right out of a children's book. Mom painted the walls a pale shade of green that set off the warm brown wood of the crib. The crib's yellow and green quilted bumper pads are still vividly imbedded in my memory. Stitched into the fabric were the animals of Noah's Ark. My favorite part of the room was the mobile. I reached up and turned it on. Six small, stuffed animals began prancing to soft music. *The baby is going to love this. I will turn it on for him or her all the time. I am going to be the best big sister ever.*

9

The baby was finally coming! It was late in the evening, just about my bedtime, when Grandma arrived to stay with Patrick and me so our parents could go to the hospital. The anticipation of a baby in the house overwhelmed me with joy. I was much too excited to think about going to sleep.

"Grandma, can I please stay up with you and wait for Dad to get home. I can't possibly sleep until I find out if I have a little brother or a little sister! Please? Please?" I begged.

"Oh Annie, you are sure excited about this baby, aren't you?"

"You have no idea, Grandma! I am going to be the best big sister ever!"

"Being a big sister is a big job, so you need a good night's sleep."

"I'm too excited to sleep, Grandma. Please let me stay up with you?" I begged. I gave her the saddest eyes I could muster.

Grandma sighed, giving in, and allowed me to lay on the couch with her and watch television. I found a pillow and curled up next to her eventually dozing off. The sound of voices woke me up: Dad and Grandma's voices. They were speaking softly in the kitchen. I couldn't make out what they were saying, but I could tell Grandma was crying. There were only two reasons I could think of as to why Grandma would be crying. Something must be wrong with the baby, or something must be wrong with my mom. *Maybe I am just having a bad dream,* I thought. I kept my eyes shut. Grandma came into the family room. I pretended to be asleep. She kissed me gently on the forehead. I listened to her footsteps as she crossed the kitchen floor. I heard the backdoor open and shut, followed by the sound of a car engine. After a few minutes, I felt the heavy weight of my dad on the couch as he sat down next to me. He placed his hand on my shoulder and gently shook me. I opened my eyes.

"Your mother will be coming home in a few days but without a baby. She had a little boy, but he died due to complications. Your mother needs a few days in the hospital to get better."

*Is this really happening? What are complications?* I didn't understand. My mind couldn't process what Dad had just said. I looked down, away from my dad's eyes, and held back tears.

"Go to bed and get some sleep, Annie."

My legs were trembling as I walked toward the attic stairs. I felt like I might throw up. I walked past Patrick's bed. He was sound asleep. I straightened up the dolls on my bed, grabbed Mrs. Beasley, got under the covers, and started to cry. The last sound I heard before falling asleep was the sound of ice cubes hitting a glass.

Before Mom came home from the hospital, Dad took apart the crib, stuffed the bedding and mobile into a garbage bag, and put it all in the garage. He moved my things down from the attic and back into my old room.

The baby's name was Eric. Grandma and Grandpa arranged to have him buried at Lakeview Cemetery in Clarkston. Mom wanted to purchase a headstone for his grave. Dad said he would take care of it. He never did. I believe that was his subtle way of punishing her for not giving him another son. Mom put the devastation of losing her baby boy into a file folder and shut the drawer. She immersed herself in projects. Dad immersed himself in a bottle of scotch.

Our parents never spoke about Eric's death. It was as if the baby had never existed. Many years later, I rode my bike to Lake View Cemetery to visit my little brother's grave. I swear I read every gravestone in that cemetery looking for his name. When I couldn't find his gravesite, I went into the cemetery office to ask for help. A nice old man looked up my baby brother's name in a box of index cards. He wrote down a number on a scratch piece of paper and told me how to find the grave. I found the number stamped on a small, round piece of concrete. I couldn't believe my baby brother didn't have a headstone. I felt as though we had just abandoned him or forgotten he had ever existed. I wanted to ask Mom why Eric didn't have a headstone, but I didn't want to upset her. I agonized for days. I had to know why he didn't have a headstone, so I finally asked.

My question took Mom by surprise. Eric had been dead for over twelve years. She told me she and Dad never got around to it. I could see the pain in her eyes. I didn't believe her, but I didn't press. In hindsight, I probably shouldn't have asked. Some files folders are better left unopened.

# Two
# Don't Play with Guns

John Berkherb, known around town as "the little man with the bit smile," was dead. Patrick and I were eating our usual breakfast of Cream of Wheat cereal when Mom announced we both had to go to his funeral.

"Why do I have to go?" Patrick complained.

"It's Kathy's birthday today. Her mom is bringing a birthday treat, so I don't want to miss school today, Mom," I whined.

"We need to go pay our respects." Mom had that firm look. She fixed her eyes on me and then on my brother challenging either one of us to dare give her any lip.

Most folks called Mr. Burkherb "the Lambert's John."

"He's the mute guy, right?" Patrick asked.

"What's a mute?" I hadn't ever heard that word before.

"Grandpa says that's what you call a guy who can't talk."

Mr. Burkherb came to live with the Lambert family in 1915 when he was about six years old.[1] The Lamberts discovered him standing barefoot in the snow. He'd been looking through a window watching them while they were having a Christmas party. Mrs. Lambert brought the boy in from the cold. John lived with them from that day on.

There was speculation around town about how a strange boy ended up just standing there in the snow in the Lambert's yard.

Some folks said his parents dumped him off in front of a nice house because they couldn't afford to feed him. Other folks thought he'd witnessed something so horrifying it rendered him stunned and speechless. Since the boy couldn't talk, he couldn't tell his story.

"Do you think anyone will ever find out why Mr. Burkherb was orphaned or why he couldn't talk?" I asked Mom as I struggled to get out of my chair with both hands on my cereal bowl.

"He probably witnessed a murder, and the killer cut out his tongue," Patrick said sticking his tongue out and wiggling it at me.

"That's enough, Patrick. Finish your breakfast and go get dressed," Mom scolded.

I was thinking about what my brother had just said. *Did someone really cut out Mr. Burkherb's tongue?* My thoughts about Mr. Burkhurb's speech issues came to an abrupt halt when I saw the dress Mom had laid out for me. The nightgown gave my hair static cling when I pulled it over my head. I tossed it in the general direction of my clothes hamper. I put on the ugly brown dress and the pair of tights. I slid my feet into my saddle shoes and dutifully tied the laces.

"I hate this dress Mom," I announced, standing in my parent's bedroom doorway watching Mom put on her lipstick.

"You look adorable in that dress Annie."

Mom always made me wear that dress when I had to get dressed up, like for family gatherings on holidays. I really hated that dress. I probably remember it so vividly some fifty years later because the one day Mom made we wear it to school just happened to be the day we had to make likenesses of ourselves. The teacher traced our bodies out on large sheets of paper. We had to cut ourselves out, draw our faces and then color in what we were wearing. When we were done, we taped the cutouts to our desk chairs. Our teacher thought it would be fun to see if our parents could pick out their child's desk at teacher conferences that night. I was the last kid in the class to finish because I had to draw and color all the squares of that ugly brown dress. God how I hated that dress!

Family gatherings usually took place at our grandparent's house. Grandma and Grandpa's house was very small, a cottage really. The house was clad in white aluminum siding and sat on a small lot on the eastern shores of Walters Lake. It had two tiny bedrooms and one bathroom. It had a "one butt" kitchen; a teeny, tiny dining room; and an enclosed porch on the lake side. Aunts, uncles, and cousins, we all jammed into the tiny space.

"Put your boots on the basement landing and your coats on my bed," Grandma said wiping her hands on her apron as she greeted us with smiles and hugs. I snuck around Mom and Dad racing Patrick to the small landing. I got my boots kicked off first, ran over to Grandpa's sitting chair, and jumped up on his lap. Grandpa had been reading the local paper when we arrived, but he set it down on the coffee table as soon as I landed on him. He placed his sturdy hands under my armpits and scooted me over onto his left knee. I picked up the newspaper.

"What's going on around Clarkston Grandpa?" I asked.

Grandpa often read the paper to me when I visited. He said it was important to stay informed about events in our community. I would sit on his knee and point to various articles, and he would read them aloud. His lap was big and soft. His breath smelled of coffee and Lucky Strike cigarettes. A headline in the paper caught my eye, "Plane crash claims 3 lives."[2] I pointed to it. Grandpa smiled at me.

"Let's read the paper later Annie." He took the paper, folded it shut, and set it back down on the coffee table.

"Why don't you go see if your grandmother needs any help in the kitchen?"

"Okay, Grandpa."

I hopped off his lap; stepped over Velvet, Grandpa's big

black lab; and skipped toward the kitchen. I spotted Toby sitting regally on the second step of the attic stairway. I stopped and sat down next to him. I could feel him start to purr as my small hand stroked his soft fur. Toby was a stray cat that Grandma had taken in. Grandpa wasn't amused when Grandma brought him in the house, but it didn't take long for the cat to steal his heart. Toby soon became Grandpa's cat. Most of our pets came to our family that way, as strays. Toby was a very large, handsome tomcat. He was a real beauty with long, black striped hair, white paws, and a white chin. The scars from his mishaps over the years only added to his charm. He had gotten himself run over by a car a few summers back. Poor guy, lost half of his tail after it was mushed by the car that struck him. Then, last summer my cousin Kristine was fishing off the dock and didn't see Toby going for the minnow on the end of her fishing pole. He swallowed that minnow in one gulp. Grandpa cut the fishing line, put Toby in the car, and rushed him to the vet. Toby had to have surgery to remove the fishhook from his stomach. His hair never grew back over the shaved area. I think the tomcat in him liked showing off his scar when he stretched out on his back.

Toby crawled up and settled onto my lap. He and I sat for a spell on the stairway. My dad and uncles were crammed in the living room watching television. Mom and her sisters were busy in the kitchen helping Grandma prepare the last of the fixings for our Thanksgiving meal. I was wearing the ugly brown dress, which was now adorned with cat hair.

"Annie, fetch Patrick and you two come and put the napkins and silver on the table," Mom hollered.

"Okay, Mom," I hollered back.

"Sorry sweet boy. Duty calls." I picked Toby up off my lap, kissed the top of his head, and set him back down on the stairs.

I stuck my head around the corner into the living room. Patrick looked up at me.

"Mom wants us to set the table."

I handed Patrick half the stack of napkins.

"Your father is still angry with me for insisting he sell his plane," I overheard Grandma say.

"I told him this morning that he is lucky he came to his senses and sold that plane because flying is dangerous. Mr. Cooley died in a plane crash just the other day. Now five children don't have their father today for Thanksgiving dinner nor will he be there on Christmas morning. I can't imagine what I would've done if your father had died when you children were small. Poor Mrs. Cooley. I'll have to bake a pie and take it over to her tomorrow."

The dinner conversation and wine flowed. Grandma and Grandpa bickered about the safety of airplane travel. Aunt Marty told us all about her new college boyfriend. She was attending Michigan State University. Aunt Janet worked at Beaumont Hospital and always had great stories to share. But Uncle John's story was the best that evening.

Uncle John's friend was a member of the Masons. The Masons met in a building in downtown Clarkston. He said his friend saw a ghost! Uncle John wasn't joshing either. He said his friend saw the actual spirit of a man wearing a long coat enter the building right through its brick exterior. Grandma poo-pooed the idea of there being any such thing as ghosts. Well, that started a good family debate. The conversation turned from Do you believe in ghosts? to Do you believe in the predictions of the *Farmer's Almanac?*. Grandpa believed in the predictions of the *Farmer's Almanac*. Mom not so much. Grandpa said the almanac predicted we would have a long, hard winter that year, and the prediction was spot on.

Snow came early, just a week or so after Thanksgiving. And lots of it too.

We were having Sunday dinner at Grandma and Grandpa's. It was just a week before Christmas. Grandma fixed stuffed peppers, Dad's favorite. But Dad made an excuse and didn't come to dinner, which he had been doing a lot lately. I knew Mom was upset about it too.

Patrick and I went sledding down the hill to the lakeshore before dinner. We wore Velvet out chasing us up and down the hill. Grandma liked us to take Velvet outside to play. A tired dog is a good dog she used to say.

"Grandpa, can we have dessert now?" I asked as Patrick and I finished clearing the dinner dishes.

"Sure Annie, but I need to talk to you and your brother first. Let's go down to my shop, shall we?"

Patrick and I exchanged a look. Only important talks with Grandpa were held in his basement workshop. Grandpa asked Patrick and me to follow him downstairs. His right hand turned the knob on the door next to the kitchen stove that led to the wooden stairway. Grandpa had big, strong hands: worker's hands. Grandpa was missing half of his middle finger. He had accidently cut it off with his bandsaw when he was working in the garage before I was born.

Grandpa proceeded down the stairs. Patrick immediately followed, but I took a moment. The stairs were steep. I didn't want to follow too close for fear of tripping. The familiar smell of gunpowder mixed with the faint odor of fish drifted into my nostrils. I reached out and grabbed the handrail. The wood, old and smooth from years of use, slid easily across the skin of my hand as I carefully began my descent. The left side of the basement was where the old coal stove and Grandpa's workbench were located. Grandpa made custom muzzle-loader guns that he sold to gun collectors. It helped pay the bills Grandma said. The machine Grandpa used to make ammunition was bolted on the right side of the bench. Sometimes he let me help him pack the BB pellets that went into the plastic gun shells. There was a beautiful blond pinup girl in a red dress hanging above the bench. The girl was from an old calendar. Grandpa either really liked the picture of that girl or he didn't care what day it was because he never updated the calendar. I suspect it was both. A large cast iron sink filled half of the basement's back wall. That was where Grandpa cleaned the fish he caught. Tucked between the iron sink and the workbench were a small washer and a dryer that Grandma used to do the wash.

Grandpa walked over to his workbench. He used his hand to brush shell casings and metal fragments off the workbench onto the basement floor. His large hands tucked under my arm pits, lifted me up, and set me on the bench. Patrick was next. My brother and I were now at his eye level. Grandpa looked at me then shifted his eyes to Patrick. The lenses in his eyeglasses made his eyes appear bigger than they actually were. His focus turned from my brother and me to the small window above his workbench.

"Your grandmother has been after me to clean out those spider webs."

Patrick and I glanced up at the window. There was no evidence of a spider. Just the webs.

Grandpa took a deep breath and let out a long sigh.

"It saddens me deeply to tell you kids that Mark Wells was accidently shot while playing with his brother yesterday."[3]

"Is he going to be okay?" I asked.

"Unfortunately, Mark died sweetheart. Such a tragic accident. Your grandmother asked that I remind you both of how dangerous guns can be. Mark and his brother were playing with a rifle they thought was empty. Mark was accidently shot in the face and killed. You kids have access to my guns every time you come down in this basement."

"We would never touch your guns Grandpa!"

"I know you wouldn't Annie or you either Patrick. Both of you bring friends here to swim and fish. You kids come down here to put fish in the sink. When your friends are visiting, it is your responsibility to make sure they never come down here alone and never come near my workbench or my guns. Do you two understand how important it is that you never allow your friends near my guns?"

"Yes, we do Grandpa." Patrick answered him. I didn't say anything, just nodded in agreement. Grandpa looked me in the eye and then looked at Patrick.

"You sure?"

"We're sure" I answered for both of us.

"Okay then. I have a sneaking suspicion your grandma has some ice cream in the freezer. Let's go check."

# Three
# Patricia Kathryn O'Connor Tisch

My mother's grandma, my Great Gramma O'Connor started her journey to heaven the same fall I started kindergarten. Her death began with the loss of a leg to diabetes. Great Gramma, confined to a wheel chair, needed constant care. Our family elders decided it would be best to move her out of her own home and into Great Uncle Jack's house. Uncle Jack lived in Berkley too, just a few blocks away from us.

"Family takes care of their own," Mom announced to Patrick and me over lunch.

"Annie, I have to take care of your great grandmother during the day while Uncle Jack is at work. That means I cannot walk you to or from school. You're going to have to start walking to and from school with Patrick."

"Patrick, I expect you to watch out for Annie, and make sure she gets to her classroom. I also expect that you will wait for her after school and walk her home."

Patrick and I sat in silence. Mom's eyes shifted from me to my brother as she waited for either of us to dare give her an argument. When no argument ensued, she began to clear the lunch dishes.

"You are such a baby," Patrick mocked when Mom was out of earshot.

I learned over the years that responding to my brother's mocking and teasing was not a good idea; it just started an argument. So, I didn't respond. Responding to him just made things worse. Funny, that has carried over into our adult years too.

As it turned out, walking to school with Patrick was not so bad, unless it rained. If it rained, he picked worms up off the sidewalk and threw them at me. I was petrified of worms for years after that. I am no longer afraid of worms. I am no longer afraid of many things.

For as long as I can remember, our family spent summer weekends at our grandparent's house on Walters Lake. My fondest childhood memories are of those days. But unlike past summers, we didn't spend the weekends of the summer of 1969 at Walters Lake. Our parents kept us busy doing other things. Mom and Dad made excuses as to why we couldn't go swimming at my grandparents' house. As it turned out, the complications Mom had experienced giving birth to baby Eric the previous summer had caused a big rift between my dad and our grandparents.

Many years later, Grandma shared with me that the complication caused life and death decisions to be made. When the delivery room doctor asked Dad to choose who would survive the birth of the baby, his wife or his son, Dad chose to let our mother die. As fate would have it, Grandpa, worried about Dad's drinking, decided to join him at the hospital and wait for the baby to arrive. Grandma told me that Grandpa threatened Dad if he didn't change his mind as to who would survive the delivery. In the end, Mom lived and Eric died.

When I was pregnant with my oldest daughter, I asked Dad about that day. I asked him if what Grandma had told me was true. Shockingly, he told me that the story, just as grandma had explained it, was true. He said the original choice he made, the choice to let Mom die, was what the Bible intended: sacrifice the mother for the son. Had the baby been a girl, Dad would have made a different choice. My dad grew up in a generation when many men believed women were the property of their husband. And that explains why he didn't want to get involved in the situation next door.

Houses in our city neighborhood were close together and didn't have central air conditioning. Cool Michigan summer breezes drifting in through open windows was nature's air conditioning. The aroma of fresh magnolia blossoms filled the air as my bedroom curtains danced in the moonlight. The sounds of nightfall lulled me to the edge of sleep. Chirping crickets, dogs barking in the distance, and the barely audible sound of a television set, blending together, created a night time symphony, leading me to slumber. The same summer evening breeze that brought in wonderful fragrance and comforting sound also brought in the desperate cries of the woman next door.

Just that morning Mrs. Beasley and I had been playing in the side yard when the nice neighbor lady came over. Her hair was the color of warm honey. She was wearing a pretty, white dress with tiny yellow flowers on it. I couldn't help but notice the bruises on her arms and face as she smiled sweetly at me. She handed me a bunch of lilacs and asked me to give the flowers to my mother.

I awoke to the sounds of my parents' raised voices. I sat up in bed, my ears straining, trying to make out the words of their argument.

"Clancy, we have to call the police! That poor woman is begging for help!"

"Mind your own business, Pat. What goes on next door is none of our concern."

My parents' argument continued for a while before Mom announced she was going to call the police.

"Patricia, I told you to stay out of it! This is none of our business!"

I had filed the morning memory of our pretty neighbor lady in a folder but pulled it out as I stood there watching Mom dial the telephone. Mom quickly hung the phone back on its cradle when she saw me.

"I can't sleep," I said rubbing my eyes.

"Why can't you sleep?"

"Because you and Dad are really loud."

"I am sorry we disturbed you, Annie. How about a glass of warm milk?"

Mom opened the refrigerator and reached for the carton of milk.

"I don't want any milk."

Mom and I stood there, studying each other for a few moments.

"Come on," Mom said as she placed her hand on the small of my back and led me back toward my bedroom, "I'll read you a story."

I loved it when Mom read to me. She always let me choose the book. This time I chose *Snow White*. We were almost to my favorite part when we heard a crashing sound from next door. We heard the nice neighbor lady cry out. I moved my body closer to my mother.

"Hold our place, sweetie. I will be right back."

Mom handed me the book. She got up off the bed, opened the door to my bedroom, and walked down the hallway. I heard the front door slam closed. *Oh boy. Is she going over there? Dad will be so mad if he finds out!* I pulled back the bedroom window curtains. I watched as Mom marched down our sidewalk, turned left, and marched right up to the front door of the next door neighbor's house.

Mom rang the nice neighbor lady's doorbell. She stood there waiting, hands on her hips. She rang the bell again impatiently. I was afraid for my mom, but I dared not get my dad because I knew how mad he would be that she had gone over there. *Oh dear God, oh dear God.* I closed my eyes and said a prayer. *Please God, don't let that mean man hurt my mom.* I opened my eyes and looked out the window toward the neighbors' house.

The front door opened. I could see the nice neighbor lady's husband in the shadow of the door. I watched the man and Mom exchange words. Mom's left hand was on her hip, and she was pointing in his face with her right. After a few minutes, the door slammed shut. Mom turned around and marched back home. I quickly closed the curtains and got back under my bed covers. Mom came back in the house, walked to my room, and sat on my bed. I handed her the book.

She let out a heavy sigh. "Now, where were we?" she asked.

"What did you say to him, Mom?"

She paused for a moment and smiled. She turned to look at me, her bright blue eyes sparkled with mischief.

"I told him that if I, or my children, heard any more fighting going on, I wouldn't call the police because my husband forbid me. But my husband didn't tell me I couldn't use his twenty-gauge Beretta to shoot a hole right through him. And I told him I was a really good shot." She winked at me.

There was no doubt that is exactly what Mom would do. My mother was true to her word and certainly no sissy.

Patricia Kathryn O'Connor Tisch was born on June 27, 1935. "Patsy" was the oldest of four children, three girls and a boy. Patsy's mother was Irish, her father, Austrian. My grandparents purchased a small house on Walters Lake in 1938. Grandpa taught Mom and her sisters how to fish, shoot, and hunt. And trust me, Mom wasn't kidding when she told the mean neighbor man that she was a very good shot. Grandpa told his girls that they could do anything boys could do, even better.

Grandma didn't approve of Grandpa's lessons. She felt girls

should act like little ladies not like boys. But it was four against one, so Grandma conceded most of the time. Nothing she could say would dissuade Grandpa from spending time with his daughters. Grandpa's hunting and fishing escapades with his girls continued. He was proud that his daughters grew up enjoying and respecting the outdoors.

There was a thoroughbred horse farm on the corner of Eston and Clarkston-Orion Roads just down the street from where my grandparents lived. From the day Mom first laid eyes on those horses, she became obsessed with the animal. She was only six years old the first time she went over to that horse farm. She climbed onto the top fence board, used an apple to coax one of the horses over to her, grabbed its mane, and hopped onto the horse's back. The horse was so stunned, it took off running at a full gallop across the pasture. Mom couldn't have been more thrilled. The owner saw Mom mounted on his prize racehorse and came running out of the barn with a lead line, capturing horse and rider. The horse's owner was not amused and told Grandpa as much. But no amount of punishment would deter her. My mom continued to sneak horse rides next door until my grandparents agreed to allow her to buy a horse of her own, probably just to keep peace with the neighbor. Mom bought Hickory with money she'd saved working odd jobs and babysitting. Trust me when I tell you that her obsession with the animal will continue until the day she draws her last breath. I think horse blood runs through her veins.

Mom graduated from Clarkston High School in 1953 with aspirations of attending veterinary school at Michigan State University. Grandma finally put her foot down. Grandma insisted Patsy start behaving like a young woman and not a boy. Boys became veterinarians, not girls. Back in the 1950s getting married right out of high school was the norm for young women. Grandma believed that women who were not married out of high school only attended college to get an "MRS." degree.

"No suitable man will marry a girl that is going to be a veterinarian!" Grandma was adamant. Mom begged Grandpa to convince Grandma to let her attend veterinary school. Grandpa's heart broke for his daughter, but in the end, he felt he had to support Grandma on the issue.

The 1950s society insinuated that if a woman was not engaged or married by her early twenties, she was in danger of becoming an "old maid." Although Mom had her own aspirations, Grandma was certainly not going to have a daughter who was an old maid. Since Mom had no proper suitors from high school, Grandma agreed to allow her to attend college for the sole purpose of meeting one. Mom could choose between nursing and teaching; veterinary medicine was off the table. Grandma warned my mother that she had better come home from college with a suitable husband. Mom attended Eastern Michigan University.

Mom graduated college with an education degree, not an *MRS.* degree. After college, she landed her first teaching job at a local Detroit elementary school. Grandma continued to pressure her to find a suitable husband. That was problematic because Mom rarely, if ever, dated. My parents met by happenstance at the wedding of their college roommates. Dad's roommate from Ohio State married Mom's roommate from Eastern Michigan. Both Mom and Dad were in the wedding party. After a short courtship, Patsy and Clancy married.

My father did not marry my mother because he truly loved her. I believe he proposed to her due to his own societal pressure. Dad had found recent success launching his own business. To complete the picture of the successful businessman, he needed a beautiful wife. Dad felt it was time to get married. He once told me he pursued my mother because she was a "real looker" and could give him handsome sons. Mom succumbed to the social pressure she felt and accepted his wedding proposal. Clancy was thirty-five years old and Patsy twenty-five when they married on her birthday, June 27, 1959. Patrick came along in 1960. I followed two years later in 1962.

# Four
# Tornado of a Move

Our parents had difficulty getting along from the start. Mom was independent. Dad was obstinate. I would often hear them argue at night after Patrick and I were in bed. Sometimes they would fight about my dad's business. Mom thought he should sell it and get a job working for someone else. Dad would not even entertain the idea. I wished he would listen to Mom. If he worked for someone else, he could be home more and not have to work Saturday's too. The topic of their arguments would eventually turn from the topic *du jour* to the topic of children. Dad felt it was Mom's duty to try to have more children. Mom refused to endure the heartbreak of losing another baby. The more Dad drank, the fiercer the arguments became. On the nights our parents fought, it was difficult for me to sleep.

There was a street light on the corner about two houses down from ours. That street lamp cast a swath of light on the front of my dollhouse. On the nights I wasn't able to sleep, Mrs. Beasley and I would sneak out of bed and play with the doll house. It was on one of those sleepless nights that the riots started.

Perhaps the stifling heat helped fuel the anger that started the Detroit riots that summer. It was Saturday, July 23rd when the chaos began. It started when police raided one of Detroit's after-hours bars just a short distance from where we lived. That police raid turned into one of the deadliest riots in United States history and lasted for almost a week.

"It will pass," was Dad's response when Mom begged him to take us out of the city to the safety of Walters Lake.

Dad downplayed Mom's concerns. He acted as if the riots were no big deal. Dad would depart in the morning for his office on Woodward Avenue leaving Mom alone with Patrick and me. She kept a brave face and did her best to keep us occupied during those horrible five days. Patrick and I played countless games of Candy Land and Rock'em Sock'em Robots. Mom wouldn't allow us to play outside during the day and ordered us to stay away from the windows after dark. While our parents watched anchorman Bill Bonds deliver updates about the riots on the television evening news, Patrick and I would sneak upstairs and watch the National Guard vehicles drive through our neighborhood. After dark, we could see fires burning in the distance. At the end of the riots forty-three people were dead, over eleven hundred were injured, and over seven thousand had been arrested. The riots destroyed more than two thousand buildings in the city. At that time, the destruction from the Detroit summer riot was surpassed only by the New York City riots during the U.S. Civil War. And the riots weren't the only destructive force that summer.[1, 2]

"Last one in is a rotten egg," Patrick yelled as he cannonballed into the water.

Dad took us for a swim while Mom prepared dinner. Our backyard butted up to a neighbor's yard, and they had an above-ground swimming pool. A chain link fence separated the two yards. Dad and some other neighbors were sitting poolside talking about the riots and politics over a couple of beers. We hadn't been in the water long when Dad screamed.

"Get out of the pool!"

My young brain was trying to process what we had gone wrong.

"Get out of the pool now!" He yelled again. "Get home, both of you!"

Dad's outburst confused me. I was certain I hadn't done anything wrong, and he hadn't been into a scotch bottle yet. I stood motionless in the water staring at him. Dad jumped into the pool, scooped me up under his right arm, and launched me onto the pool deck.

"Get home as fast as you can. NOW!"

Patrick, like a frightened racoon, scurried out of the pool and onto the deck as fast as he could. My brother I scrambled down the pool deck stairs and took off running toward the fence that separated our two yards. We ran as fast as we could. I was scared and confused, tears streamed down my face. The wind was really picking up, slowing my progress. Patrick was older and faster than I was. He ran past me and quickly climbed over the fence. I felt Dad's strong hands reach under my armpits. He picked me up and tossed me over the fence. I hit the ground on my left side. "Get up! Run!" Dad yelled hopping over the fence himself and landing on both feet in our back yard.

I pushed myself up off the grass and ran. Heading across the back yard toward our house, I watched Patrick as he struggled to pull open the white storm door against the strong wind. Reaching us, Dad grabbed us both and pulled us in close to his chest. He reached out and grabbed the handle of the storm door. He muscled the door open against the wind. The thin, white storm door stood no chance. The wind pulled it right out of our dad's hand. The door broke right off its hinges; the wind sent it blowing down the driveway. We ran into the house as Dad slammed and locked the thick wood back door behind us.

The day turned dark, as if night had fallen in a matter of seconds. I didn't understand what was happening. I was scared and confused. Meeting us on the landing at the top of the basement stairs, Mom looked as scared and confused as I was.

Our mom and dad exchanged a look.

"Patsy, we need to get down in the basement now." Dad was calm but firm.

I knew it must be serious because Mom didn't give him an argument. And she always gave Dad an argument. Mom rushed down the stairs with the three of us close on her heels. Moments after we got downstairs, rain started pounding against the basement windows. My insides rattled along with the house.

As it turned out, our father was neither drunk nor angry that afternoon. He and the other dads had spotted the funnel cloud that would turn into an F3 tornado, one of the worst to hit the area since an F5 in 1952, which injured over eight hundred people. Fifty-four people in our neighborhood got hurt that hot summer day, but thankfully, there were no fatalities.[3]

Patrick waited out the storm roller-skating relentlessly around the basement. Mom and Dad waited out the storm sitting in aluminum folding lawn chairs. I waited out the storm on Mom's lap. She was the first one of us to break the silence. Turning to my dad she announced, "We're moving."

He didn't give her any argument. They purchased forty acres of vacant land in Clarkston.

The Isle of Man is a small piece of land that lies in the Irish Sea between England, Ireland, Scotland, and Wales. Great Gramma O'Connor told me Irishman Finn MacCooill created the island. The story goes that, while Finn was battling with a Scot, he threw a chunk of earth from Ireland toward Scotland. The chunk of earth landed in the Irish Sea and became the Isle of Man. My Irish relatives were famous for their tall tales, so I knew Great Gramma's story was questionable, or if nothing else, exaggerated.

According to O'Connor family folklore, Isle of Man native James Carran came to the New World sometime around 1827 and married a young lass named Annie (my namesake). It was their son who came to Clarkston, Michigan as one of our town's first settlers. William "Billy" Allen and his wife, Lydia, purchased two hundred and eighty acres on what is now Allen Road and built their dream farm back in 1884.[4]

According to L.D. Reilly, the old man my parents bought the property from, the Allen farmhouse, barns, and adjacent out buildings burned down without explanation sometime in the early 1900s. My parents purchased the ruins of the farmstead in 1968, including the forty acres surrounding it. The farm's original silo stands to this day. An icon of the farm's Irish roots.

# Five
# Night Terrors

M om was analyzing the design retouches for the Allen Road house when Grandma and Grandpa stopped by for a glass of Port. Patrick and I were engaged in a game of checkers.

"This house is awful big and I image quite expensive," Grandpa said as Dad walked him through the pages of blueprints.

"No reason to be concerned, John. My company is doing well, and I can afford it."

"Why do you need such a big house, Clarence? Ruth and I raised four children in our small house, and they turned out just fine."

Grandpa was a practical man. His son-in-law was not. Patrick and I spent the evening playing checkers and listening to the two men argue. Grandpa tried to convince Dad to build a smaller, less expensive home. Dad tried to convince Grandpa that he could afford to build his wife the dream house she wanted. But trust me, Dad's stubbornness on the issue had nothing to do with pleasing my mother. It had everything to do with proving to Grandpa that he was a successful businessman.

Construction of the Allen Road house launched in early spring and continued late into the fall. Patrick and I spent every weekend with Mom at the construction site. When school let out for the summer, Mom took us to the construction site every day, unless it rained. It was the best, and worst, school summer vacation I can remember. Mom recruited me to sand and stain what seemed to me to be endless pallets of walnut beams and birch paneling. Patrick had the worst job: digging fence post holes for the horse paddock with an old, rusted posthole digger. I was horrified the first time I had to use the field as a bathroom, but I soon adapted to using the great outdoors as a toilet, and now possess a lifelong skill. It was quite a culture shock when we eventually moved from a small bungalow in the city to a thirty-two hundred square foot house on forty acres in the middle of nowhere. Mom and Dad seemed so happy that year; 1970 was a new decade full of possibilities.

"Hey! It's Grandma!" I announced dropping my sandpaper and running toward the soon-to-be enclosed garage. Grandma's new Tornado was kicking up dust as it rounded the second corner of our long driveway.

"Hi, Grandma!" I shouted, waving as I ran up to her car door.

"Hi sweetheart. Come here and give me a hug. Let me see your hands."

I leaned in through the driver's side window, put my arms around my grandma's small frame, and gave her a squeeze. She took my small hands into hers turning them over and inspecting them. "Your young hands shouldn't be used for man's labor!" Grandma gave me her *look*.

"It's okay Grandma. I don't mind helping."

"I came to see if your mother would give you and your brother a break from your slave labor to participate in clean-up day at the beach."

"Hi, Mom," our mother said as she approached Grandma's car.

"The residents on the lake are having our annual clean-up of Sunny Beach, and I was hoping Patrick and Annie could come and help."

"There are a lot of boards to be sanded and post holes to be dug, Mom."

"Your father and brother said they would be out to help you

tomorrow, Patsy. Please give the children a break, and let them come with me."

"Please, Mom, please?" I begged, jumping up and down.

The two women had some kind of secret conversation with their eyes. I waited impatiently for a decision.

"Alright, go get your suits," Mom sighed.

"Would you mind feeding them dinner too?"

"My pleasure, dear." Grandma glanced in my direction, giving me a wink.

"Thanks, Mom!" I ran off to fetch Patrick.

Patrick jumped in the front seat of Grandma's car. I jumped in the back, bathing suit and goggles in hand. Sitting on the back seat next to me was a bag of groceries from Rudy's Market. Sticking out the top of the shopping bag was the newspaper. The headline read "Boy killed on way to school".[1] I took the paper out of the shopping bag and opened it.

The paper reported that Charles Priebe, an eighth grader at Clarkston Junior High, was killed on school property. Witnesses said Charles appeared to be looking back at something when he stepped backwards right into the path of a school bus. Grandma and I were at Rudy's Market a few weeks later when I overheard some boys talking about the accident. One of the boys saw it happen. He said it seemed like Charles was backing away from something when he walked in front of the school bus. It was as if he was backing away from something no one else saw. *Backing away from an evil spirit,* I thought.

I folder the paper and put it back in the shopping bag. I sat quietly in the back seat as Grandma's car traversed the curves on Clarkston Orion Road, heading towards Walters Lake. I had enjoyed spending this summer in Clarkston, but something about the town made me uneasy. I didn't know exactly why; it just did. Reading the article about Charles Priebe's death didn't help. Just a few weeks earlier I'd overheard my grandparents talking about a little girl getting killed when her bicycle collided with a car on Maybee Road. Her name was Renee Cox as I recall. Funny how some things just stick in your mind while other things just float straight away.

After picking up what seemed like hundreds of beer cans on Sunny Beach, Grandma finally let us quit. We dropped our garbage bags and ran as fast as we could to our grandparents' house. I was close on my brother's heels as he sprinted through the backyard and ran down the dock. Patrick cannonballed into the lake. I cannonballed in right behind him. The water was cool on my sweaty skin. I surfaced, tasting the salt from my sweat as I wiped the water off my face. Velvet jumped in the lake with us. She had a tree stick in her mouth. My arms stroked through the water toward her.

"Silly old dog."

Grandma had given us forty-five minutes to swim while she prepared dinner. We played around in the water throwing sticks for Velvet. That dog never tired of jumping off the dock to fetch sticks. Grandma served us the usual summer weekday fare for dinner. Pan-fried lake perch and fried canned white potatoes accompanied by a fresh vegetable she'd picked up at Pierre's Orchard. I put the death of the young boy killed by a school bus in a file folder and shut the drawer. It had been a long day. I was tired and sunburned. I was ready to go home.

We were half-heartedly contemplating playing a game of checkers while we waited for Mom to pick us up. Patrick was laying on the floor petting Velvet. I was sitting quietly on the love seat, my knees pulled up to my chest, nightgown pulled over my legs. Grandma was crocheting another one of her beautiful afghans. I never tired of watching her small hands work yarn through the two long hooks. She made the task look effortless. She tried to teach me how to crochet many times. I didn't have the dexterity nor the patience. Grandpa sat quietly reading a hunting magazine. A storm was approaching. Brilliant flashes of light shot across the dark sky above the lake every few minutes. Low, rolling thunder followed each flash. It wouldn't be long until the rain started. Grandpa set the magazine down, lit a cigarette, and gazed outside watching the storm roll in.

"I don't think it's a good idea if the kids walk up to the dairy alone any more, Ruth."

"Don't overreact, John," Grandma responded not looking up from her crocheting.

"Why don't you want us to walk up to the dairy alone anymore, Grandpa?" I asked.

"Your grandfather is just a worry wort. Go on over and sit on his stool. I am sure he won't be able to resist running a brush through that beautiful hair of yours." Grandma looked up and smiled at me.

Grandpa chuckled and patted the stool. Grandma set down her needles and yarn and went to fetch a hairbrush. I scurried across the porch floor and sat down atop the green velvet stretched tightly across the top of a small three-legged stool. Grandpa's big hands made short order of the hair tie that held my damp hair in a ponytail. Grandma handed him a hairbrush and went back to her crocheting. Grandpa's large left hand lightly stroked my head in between each pass with the hairbrush he made with his right. It was as if the love in his heart transferred to me through his hands. The ritual was comforting and peaceful.

Grandpa's concern for our safety had stemmed from a recent incident in town. The paper reported that two local boys were forced into a stranger's car at gunpoint and sexually assaulted.[2] One of the boys got shot in the back while attempting to escape.[3] Something evil had come to Clarkston alright. And the police had no idea who, or what, it was.

# Six
# Allen Road

Patrick was jumping out of his skin with excitement the day we finally moved into the Allen Road house. He loved being outside exploring the vast areas of open land, forests, and deer trails. I had an uneasy feeling. I could feel the anxiety in my stomach. Like butterflies, but not the good kind.

Dad arranged for his company men to come with two trucks and move our belongings. Mom seemed so happy. We didn't have much, so it took the men no time at all to load our things. Mom's station wagon was stuffed full of clothes. Patrick rode in the front seat; Smokey the cat and I were crammed in the back. I waved goodbye to the small house on Phillips Street as we pulled out of the driveway for the last time.

The nightmares started shortly after we moved into the new house. My parents told me it was normal after moving to an unfamiliar environment and that they would go away once I settled in.

"I miss our old house," I said as Mom tucked me into bed.

"You don't like your new room with your great big closet?"

"I like my room, Mom. It's just kind of scary here."

"There is nothing to be scared about, Annie. You just have to get used to all this open space is all."

"Seems like lots of bad things happen here, Mom."

"Don't worry; it's not good for you. Clarkston has just had a couple of unusual incidents recently. Maybe you should stop reading the newspaper with your grandfather. Accidents happen everywhere sweetheart. There is nothing to be scared about. You just need to settle in here is all."

Mom's soft lips kissed my forehead. She tucked the bed covers in nice and snug like a burrito around Mrs. Beasley and me.

"Well, look who's here." Mom picked up Smokey and set him on the bed. Smokey circled around the foot of my bed a few times before he settled down. The sweet old tabby cat began his nightly grooming ritual. Aunt Janet called it "cat's doing his laundry."

"Don't forget to say your prayers," Mom whispered as she softly shut my bedroom door.

I didn't forget to say my prayers. I prayed every night that God would keep me and my family safe. I prayed to God that He let me sleep through the night without any nightmares. I prayed for my guardian angel to keep a magic force field around me so nothing could *get me*.

In an attempt to avoid nightmares, I often avoided sleep. That night was no exception. I crept quietly out of bed and went over to my dollhouse. The full moon cast a soft light through the large windows. It was as if God himself had turned on a lamp for me. The dollhouse was familiar and welcoming in my new big bedroom.

My parents moved out to the country to try to make a fresh start, leaving the memories of two miscarriages, the death of a baby son, the Detroit riots, and a tornado behind them. Although most people have never heard of Clarkston, Michigan, we locals boast that our town is the former home of Valerie Bertinelli, Tim Robbins, and Bob Seger, and the current home of Kid Rock. If you visit either one of our three downtown restaurants, you will learn two have been featured on the Food Network show *Diners, Drive-Ins, and Dives*. At one time, we had the largest barn in Michigan. At least that's what the local folks said about the Ellise barn.[1] The barn was built in 1893, and the loft could hold 4,000 bales of hay. The Ellises found a basket on their front porch with a baby in it. That is how they got their son Glen.[2]

The village of Clarkston is the epitome of small town America. We have a main street with historic homes and a small town center complete with quaint shops. Rudy's market broadcasts the Detroit Tiger's baseball games into Main Street on game days. Residents rarely miss the annual Fourth of July parade, kicked off with the National Anthem and followed by the local high school marching band. Parade participants include the local 4-H club, antique car clubs, amateur floats, and lots of candy is thrown to the kids. To outsiders, Clarkston is a charming village, the kind of town you would want to be from. But sometimes things aren't always as they appear. Just because something seems a certain way doesn't mean it really is.

The Standring's were hosting a party in their home that spring. Eric Standring, a sophomore at Clarkston High School, accompanied family friend Paul Lammonds from the party to Paul's home to fetch a guitar. Two hours later, Eric returned covered in blood and incoherent. Deputies found Paul Lammonds' body in his home. He'd been beaten to death.[3] Eric had never been in trouble before that night, at least that's what I heard. No one knew what came over the boy to make him do what he did. Paul's early, tragic, and unexplained death was the first of many to come in our idyllic small town.

My Uncle John was one of our town's volunteer firefighters. He was my mom's younger brother. I was at his house playing with my cousins when the dispatcher called for him to assist at the scene of a car crash. He never said anything about the crash when he came back several hours later. But I guessed he'd gone to the accident I read about in the paper just a few days later. Two village kids were dead. First responders arrived on Waterford Hill to find the 1963 Tempest in which some kids were riding torn in half. Mark Fearnow and Maribeth Jones were both just sixteen years old, when they died.[4] The kid who was driving died too. He wasn't from Clarkston though. He probably should have stayed away from here.

Marty, short for Margaret, was my mother's baby sister. She's how I got my middle name. Aunt Marty's friend Gerry Dark was swimming with friends in the mill pond when he apparently slipped as he was about to dive. Gerry suffered a fractured neck.[5] The small charming village we had just moved to seemed to be having some troubles all right. "All towns have their troubles" my mom would say any time I expressed my concern. Maybe she was right. And in spite of its troubles, Clarkston had some fun things going on. Like the Village Days Festival.

"Maybe we should just park at the church and walk to the festival, Clancy. It's not that far for goodness sake," Mom suggested trying to keep the annoyance out of her voice.

It was Dad's third pass down Holcomb Street.

"Just let us out. We will meet you." Mom was getting extremely irritated.

I don't think Dad was trying to find the closest parking spot to the festival possible to please her. He would do the exact opposite of whatever she wanted him to do. It was his way of thinking he was controlling her. But there is not a force on earth that can control my mother. She lit a cigarette and blew the smoke toward him.

"Jesus, Pat. When are you going to stop smoking those things?"

I could feel a fight brewing. Her frustration was growing by the minute. Dad pulled up next to a pickup truck and put the car into reverse.

"For God's sake, Clarence. You can't fit in that spot!"

"I got it, Pat!" Dad snapped as he bumped into the truck.

"Good job." Mom rolled her eyes.

After what seemed like an eternity of Dad backing up, pulling forward, and inching his way into the tight parking spot, he finally put his Plymouth Fury in park. Patrick and I threw open our doors and jumped out.

"Come on, hurry up! We are going to miss the start of the race!" Patrick hollered as he started running down the sidewalk toward the beach.

I stood on the sidewalk waiting for our parents. They were still in the car arguing. Patrick stopped running. He stood on the sidewalk dancing from foot to foot, anxiously waving for me to come along. I started to walk toward him.

Village Days Festival was an annual event held in downtown Clarkston over the three days of Labor Day weekend. There were games, prizes, and food. Mom liked to attend the festival for the sidewalk sales at the two clothing stores. Dad liked to walk around to the local merchants to gather raffle tickets. Dad was an eternal optimist. Every year he was convinced he would win a raffle prize in the drawing following Monday's parade, but he never did. There was a carnival set up in the village parking lot with booths selling all kinds of stuff. There was a street dance on Sunday night. Patrick and I ran around town with the Freitag twins and our neighbors Patty and Jerry while our parents drank and danced. My favorite part of the festival was the parade on Monday morning. Patrick's favorite part of the festival was the corn roast at the American Legion after the parade.

The festival was winding down. We were at the last event of the holiday weekend. Patrick's favorite, the corn roast. Dad was complaining that he hadn't won a raffle prize again this year. I was biting into my first ear of corn.

"Those darn raffles are rigged."

"I think Mom would call you a sore loser, Dad," I commented with a mouth full of corn.

"*Touche'*, Annie," Mom laughed. "And don't talk with your mouth full."

A friend of Mom and Dads strolled up and joined us at the picnic table.

"Hey, J.W. Nice to see you."

"Nice to see you too, Pat. Hello, Clancy." J.W. set down his paper plate and swung his legs under the picnic table, taking a seat next to me.

"Did y'all hear about Jim McVeigh?" J.W. asked

"Didn't hear a thing, J.W." Dad replied.

"Jim is in critical condition at the hospital due to some freak accident he had while working on his car. The damnedest thing I ever heard. Neighbors are saying the car just fell on him. No explanation for the car to just fall on him like that either." J.W. reported. "It's the same thing that happened to Bill Merenuk. Remember that? Bill got pinned under his car in his garage when the jack slipped out for no apparent reason. Figured you might know something more, Pat, considering your brother volunteers for the fire department and all."[6, 7]

J.W. was not J.W.'s real name. It was short for something. Short for what I have no idea. Not only was his name short, he was short. Short and stocky. He wore his hair greased back, like Elvis Presley. His mouth was too big for his face. When he smiled, he looked like The Joker from *Batman*. J.W. was from somewhere in the south and had a real strong southern accent. Dad said he talked like a hillbilly. J.W. and his wife came to the Detroit area to work for one of the automotive companies. They had a cute little baby. I liked J.W.'s accent and his friendly personality.

"Why don't you boys finish this discussion while getting us some more corn?" Mom suggested giving J.W. a stern look.

"How is your corn, sweetie?" Mom asked me, obviously trying to distract me from the conversation.

I set my half-eaten ear of corn down on my plate. Looking at J.W., I asked, "Do you think it is odd that so many people die round here?"

"I don't think more people die here than anywhere else, little lady." J.W. smiled at me with that big grin of his. "It's the *way* they are dying around here that spooks me!" He laughed.

"J.W. Beasley!" Mom scolded.

J.W. laughed again as he put his arm around me.

"You know I am just kidding ya, don't you, little lady?"

I didn't respond. I didn't see the humor in the fact that some guy almost died in his garage. Not at all. Not even a little darn bit. I picked up my plate, got up from the picnic table, and went in search of a garbage can. I spotted Doreen and some other girls kicking a ball around. I tossed my plate in the trash and ran to join them.

It was probably a good thing I didn't stay at the table and listen to the adults' next conversation. Another neighbor stopped by the table asking my parents if they'd heard the news that Gerry Frich shot himself in his car at a local park.[8]

Labor Day's blazing sun was starting to set. Mom gathered us all up to go home. Patrick wanted to say longer, but Mom said no. The first day of school of the new school year was the next day. Mom drove home. Dad was too drunk to drive.

Anxiety about starting a new school year made it hard for me to fall asleep. It had been an incredibly hot day, and the night brought little relief. There was barely a breath of a breeze. My thoughts went back to the day's corn roast. Back to what J.W. had said about that man who was almost killed in his garage for no reason. I wished we hadn't moved to Clarkston.

*The canopy of my bed was falling. I tried to get out of bed, but I couldn't move. It was as though something was holding me down. The yellow fabric fell over my face. I was finding it hard to breathe. I tried to scream, but nothing would come out.*

I awoke from the nightmare with a start. Sweat dampened my skin; my legs tangled up in bedsheets. It took a few moments for my mind to clear and my breathing to slow. I looked around my room, which was bathed in moonlight. The windows were open. My pale-yellow canopy's fabric was swaying ever so slightly in the breeze. The sound of crickets and bull frogs drifted in from the outdoors. I was thirsty. I untangled my legs from the bedsheets, careful not to disturb Smokey. I snuck quietly to the bathroom. I shut the bathroom door before I turned on the light. I used the toilet and got a drink of water. I turned off the light and went back to bed.

The nightmares started as occasional bad dreams. The bad dreams escalated into frequent nightmares. The frequent nightmares escalated into night terrors. One night I sat upright in bed screaming in distress, scaring my mother half to death. The only thing I remember was how scared she looked when she woke me up. I couldn't remember anything about the night terror itself. My nightgown was soaked with sweat. My heart was pounding. Coincidently, that first night terror happened on the same day Russell Trim drown while swimming in Foley Pond off White Lake Road.[9] Perhaps that was just a coincidence, but I do not believe in coincidences. Mom tried to rationalize that the stress of the move was causing my nightmares. She was convinced they would end as soon as I settled into the tranquil countryside that was Allen Road.

# Seven
# A Visit to the Emergency Room

I was up early even though I hadn't slept much the night before. The sound of my parents arguing stopped my downward progress on the last step of the stairway. Mom was talking.

"A dog might help her feel more secure, Clancy."

"Dogs are a lot of trouble, Pat."

"Trouble for whom? You? You are rarely home. The children and I are out here on this property alone all day, and a dog would be good protection."

I sat on the steps listening for Dad's reply. I crossed my fingers. *Please Jesus, make him say it is okay for us to get a dog.*

"Clancy, I am done arguing about it. We need a dog. I am sure my brother could help us get a pup from one of his hunting buddies."

"If John can get you a puppy, and it isn't too expensive, then I guess it's alright. But the children need to learn responsibility and take care of it."

*A puppy! Patrick will be so excited. He's been bugging Mom and Dad for years to get a dog.* It took all my self-control not to tell him what I overheard. Mom didn't like me eavesdropping, even if it was by accident. A few weeks later, my Uncle John showed up at our house with a chocolate brown Labrador puppy. Patrick named her Sadie.

The topic of our parent's squabbles turned from getting a dog to getting a mailbox. Mom had been pestering Dad for months to put one up. She was fed up with the drive to town every day to the post office to get our mail. Dad, tired of her nagging on the subject, sent one of his workers out to the farm to put up a box. Ours was the fourth mailbox on Allen Road. At first it was fun to walk down the long drive and get the mail and newspaper, but the novelty didn't last long.

"Hi, Mom!" I yelled slamming the back door.

"Hi, sweetie. Dinner will be ready soon, so please wash up. Where is your brother?"

"He and Jerry are having a pear fight."

"Did you remember to fetch the mail on your way home?"

"Sorry, Mom. I forgot."

"Well, I guess you better turn around and go get it then."

"I'm tired and hungry. I don't want to go get the mail. Make Patrick go do it."

"I asked you. Now go on," she said, gently placing her hands on my shoulders, turning me around, and pushing me toward the back door.

Before moving out to Allen Road Mom boarded her horses at a farm in Oxford. Dad's crew built a barn on our property after we moved in. Seemed to take them forever, but when it was finally finished, Mom and Aunt Janet brought the horses to the farm. It took the horses a while to settle in, kind of like me.

Randy and Tazra were trotting along the fence line as I started down the driveway. It was late afternoon. I didn't inherit Mom's obsession with the animal, but those two magnificent horses trotting along the fence line was an incredible sight. The sun was sinking; its light reflected off their chestnut brown hair. Remnants of the old pear orchard lined the right side of our drive. Patrick and a neighbor boy were picking up fallen pears and throwing them at one another. Their pear fight was what had the horses spooked, causing them to trot about. I was halfway down the long driveway when a pear came within inches of my head.

"Almost got ya!" Patrick yelled, laughing.

I darted into the orchard and hid behind one of the trees. Looking down, I pushed the tall grass around with my foot until I found a fallen pear. I picked up the piece of fruit, jumped out from behind the tree, and threw it as hard as I could in the direction of my brother. I missed him by a long shot.

Patrick laughed, "You throw like a girl." He returned my assault with a pear of his own. It came closer than my shot, but I was able to dodge the fruit with ease.

Continuing my stroll down the driveway, I noticed the sky. It was a beautiful shade of sapphire blue. I couldn't help but admire the perfectly formed fluffy, white clouds. Just a wisp of breeze moved them, slowly changing their shapes as they drifted effortlessly in the sky. On days like these, I could almost convince myself there was nothing here to be afraid of.

Mr. Harris waved at me as he passed by. I held my breath and turned my head, waiting for the dust his truck kicked up to blow away. I crossed the dirt road to our mailbox. We hadn't had the mailbox very long, but it already had a big dent in the side. Some local boys came down the road one night and smashed it with a baseball bat. Did the same thing to Mr. Harris's mailbox too. He had already replaced his. Ours still had a big dent, and the flag was missing. Mom had to nag for months until Dad delegated the task and someone fixed it.

My small arm had to go halfway into the mailbox in order for my fingers to reach the mail. *Why does the mailman have to shove it all the way in the back?* I asked myself. I got the paper out of the paper box. As I walked up the driveway, I opened the paper: "Tot drowns in Townsend Lake."[1] Little Donna Aldrich's mom noticed she was missing and found her twenty minutes later in the lake. The sheriff and Dr. O'Neill tried to resuscitate the child but she died anyway.

I folded the paper, put it under my left arm, and headed toward the house.

*I was right on my brother's heels as he ran down our grandparents' dock. He cannonballed into the lake, and I jumped in right behind him. The water was cool on my sweaty skin. I started to paddle toward the surface. I could see the sunlight dancing on the water just a few feet above. Only a few more strokes and I will be on the surface. I kicked my feet and continued toward the surface of the water, but the surface wasn't getting any closer. I swam harder. The surface still wasn't getting any closer. I could feel my lungs starting to burn. I needed air. I was starting to panic. I am going to drown. Oh God, I am going to drown.*

Shooting straight up in bed, I drew in a big breath of air. *That was a bad one*, I thought.

It took a few moments for me to orient myself. Smokey was not in his usual spot. I pulled back the covers and got out of bed. Opening my bedroom door, I headed down the hallway. Sadie was asleep at the top of the stairs. The dog opened her big brown eyes and acknowledged my presence with a stretch and a yawn. I stepped over her and proceeded down the stairs. Mom and Dad's bedroom was at the bottom of the stairway. I tiptoed quietly passed their open door on my way to the kitchen. I was thirsty. I often awoke from nightmares and night terrors thirsty. I opened the refrigerator door and found it stocked full of beer and soda pop. Mom and Dad were expecting company the next evening, some guy from Dad's company and his son. My parents expected me to entertain the boy. *Why doesn't Patrick have to entertain the stupid kid,* I thought, grabbing a bottle of Coca-Cola. I shut the refrigerator door.

Dad often invited business associates out to the Allen Road farm. He liked to impress people with how successful he was. I experienced my first trip to the emergency room complements of the stupid kid I had to entertain. I didn't like the kid from the second I laid eyes on him. Anyone with two working neurons could tell the kid was a brat within one minute of meeting him. Dad told me to take him outside and play. There was a big sand pile on the side of the house that the mason left when the house was built. I thought the sand pile would be a good place to entertain the awful boy. The awful boy thought it was a good idea to hit me in the head with a brick he'd found buried deep in the sand.

Lost in my thoughts, just pushing sand into a plastic bucket, I didn't even see the blow coming. I put my hand up to the spot of the blow on my forehead, pulled my hand away, and didn't notice any blood. *Darn that hurt.* I wanted to go in the house and tell on the kid, but I knew my parents would get angry. My parents' rule was we were not allowed to come and tattle or whine on each other unless there was blood involved.

"That was mean," I said.

The awful boy didn't say anything back. He just glared at me. I turned my attention back to filling up the plastic pail. I noticed a few drops of blood hitting the sand. I put my hand back up to my forehead then pulled it away. This time my hand was covered in blood. Even though I would have liked nothing more than to deck that kid, I somehow found the moral compass my parents had instilled in me. Instead of punching the awful boy in the face, I stood up and walked away.

Entering the house through the porch sliding door, I started toward my parents' bathroom. Shutting their bathroom door behind me, I looked around for something to temporarily stop the bleeding while I found a BAND-AID. I picked up a washcloth from the counter and pressed it to my forehead. I looked up in the mirror. After a few moments, I removed the cloth. There was a goose egg forming on my forehead with a huge gash in the middle of it. I placed the washcloth over the wound while I searched the vanity drawers for the box of BAND-AIDs.

Needing to use both hands to open the box of bandages, I had to set the washcloth down. Blood started running down my face. I took the largest size bandage from the box, peeled back the paper and tape, and applied it over the gash. I threw the bloody washcloth in the hamper and went back outside. I wasn't outdoors long when I felt blood streaming down my face. *The BAND-AID must not be big enough.* I went back into the house, back to the bathroom, and got a second BAND-AID. I placed it over the first. I hadn't even made it to the sliding door when blood started rolling down my face again. I was reluctant to interrupt my parents, but I seriously needed my mom.

"Dear Lord!" Mom exclaimed when I walked into the living room.

"What happened?"

"The kid hit me in the head with a brick."

The awful boy's father apologized to my parents and set off to find his obnoxious son. Dad and his business associate were well into a bottle of scotch by the time of the incident, so Mom had to drive me to the hospital by herself. She had me lie down on the front seat with my head in her lap. She applied pressure to the wound with her right hand while she steered the car with her left.

The entire front of my shirt was covered in blood by the time we arrived at the hospital. Mom pulled the truck up right in front of the emergency room doors, turned it off, and carried me inside. A nurse ran up to us. It all happened so fast. It seemed like just a few moments passed before I was on a table, my face covered with a cloth. I couldn't see anything, and I was scared.

I felt the sting of a needle going into my forehead. I started to cry. Mom held my hand and tried to comfort me. Lots of people were talking, but none of them were talking to me. One of the voices poured a liquid substance into the wound, and it stung real bad. I could feel the needle going into my forehead with each stitch. The entire ordeal was horrifying. The scar that was quite prominent on my forehead at one time now just blends in with the wrinkles.

# Eight
# Clancy

During the first week in our new school, I encountered a different species of mankind that I had never met before. Mean girls. My therapist asked me during one of our sessions if I had experiences in my life that led me to believe that I was defective in some way. She asked me if I could recall any instances of being teased or humiliated by my peers. I pulled open a long-closed drawer and pulled out a file.

I was eleven when Mom insisted I wear a training bra.

The first day Mom made me wear the training bra to school, one of the mean girls started a rumor that I was "stuffing." I'll never forget the humiliation of being in chorus class when the mean girl announced loudly, "It sure is stuffy in here." The children in the class starting whispering and snickering. It took all of my self-control not to burst into tears. The teasing continued for the rest of the school year. Girls followed me into the girl's bathroom and pushed and shoved while trying to pull up my shirt. I was challenged on the playground to pull up my shirt and prove to everyone that I didn't stuff. I never told my parents about the bullying. I just endured it. Nobody likes a tattletale.

Patrick had a much easier time making friends than I did. The first friend he made was Billy. Billy's father owned the town's local funeral home. Billy's family lived in an apartment on the second floor. I spent many weekend evenings drinking slow gin fizzes in that apartment above the funeral home during my high school years. Billy turned out to be one of my closest friends. He was lots of fun and easy to talk too. Billy and I, like most of the kids I hung out with, partied a bit too hard. Perhaps the drugs and alcohol helped us keep our file drawers shut. Or perhaps it was just the era we were growing up in: sex, drugs, and rock-and-roll.

Billy frequently spent the night at our house when the boys were young. He and Patrick would play outside for hours on end. Mom practically had to drag them in for lunch. Those two boys had more fun in the winter than any kids I have ever known. They spent hours and hours building snow forts. Winters in Michigan can be exceptional. An elegant landscape of snow and ice. And when you're a kid, there's nothing better than a Great Lakes snow storm.

We had been in the midst of a snow storm, and school had been closed most of the previous week. I woke up feeling peaceful and rested. I hadn't had any night terrors in a few weeks. It was Sunday. *I wonder what time it is,* I thought stretching my arms above my head. The temperature was brutally cold. I pulled back the covers, got out of bed, and trotted over to the window to survey the landscape. *What a marvelous day!* Each pine tree branch was weighed down with inches of fluffy, white snow. Paths of small animal tracks wove around the base of the trees and then scattered across the backyard pond. Snow piled perfectly on the top boards of the pasture fence. There was not a breath of wind. The sun was shining. *Looks like a great day for skating.*

Three other families lived on Allen Road. Several other families lived on neighboring Reese Road. Each family had a couple of children. That meant Patrick and I could usually get a handful of kids to help shovel the ice. After being cooped up in the house for days, I was chomping at the bit to get outside. Taking the stairs two at a time, I ran and looked out the large front window. Much to my disappointment, "the guy" had come and plowed our driveway, which meant my parents could drive to church, which meant I had to go to church, and I didn't like church.

I endured Mass, had lunch, and had been sledding when the neighbor kids finally showed up to help shovel the snow off the ice to skate. By that time, Dad was a few inches into a bottle of scotch. The snow was deep and extremely heavy. Even though there were five of us, we were struggling to push the snow off the ice. Just when we were about to give up, I saw Dad, sauced up, riding his 1939 Ford tractor straight toward us. I turned to Nancy, one of the neighbor kids, "This isn't going to end well."

Before I explain how it ended, you first need to understand a bit about my father.

Clarence Edward Johns was born in 1925 in Cuyahoga Falls, Ohio. He was the third youngest of nine children. They all lived in a two-room house with no indoor plumbing. Clancy's parents, like many folks during the depression, were extremely poor. Mom told me Dad's family was so poor that he had to share a pair of shoes with one of his brothers. Dad rarely opened the file of memories from his childhood. If he did, he kept those memories to himself. We visited Dad's family just once in my lifetime, when I was in my twenties. That one visit with my aunts, my dad's sisters, provided much insight into the man he had become.

According to his sisters, my dad was an excellent baseball player with aspirations of playing for the major leagues. My dad's father did not approve of playing games. Times were hard and there were many mouths to feed. Dad was to come straight home after school to help his father run the family carpentry business. Against his father's orders, Dad had attended ball practice every day after school. When he eventually got home from ball practice, my grandfather would ask him where he had been. Dad was very stubborn and defiant. He would look my grandfather straight in the eye and say, "Ball practice." His dad would give him a whooping with a belt for his disobedience. As baseball season continued, Dad's disobedience continued, and the discipline became more severe. Dad knew he was going to get a whooping when he got home, but his love for the game of baseball was stronger than his fear of the beatings.

Eventually, Dad began to stutter when asked where he had been after school. He didn't want to answer the question, but he couldn't lie. My father always stuttered when he got nervous. And until the day he died at the age of ninety-one, he was still just as stubborn.

Now that you have an understanding about how stubborn my father was, you can understand that no matter how hard we kids tried to convince him that taking his 1939 Ford tractor on the ice was not a good idea, he would do it anyway. At first it was just a sound, like the sound of a gunshot, as the ice began to crack. The left rear tire went through the ice first. I stood there near the shore, motionless, afraid if I took a breath it would somehow create an imbalance that would break the ice. The tractor just sat there on top of the ice, listing to the left. Dad sat very still. Another crack. The right tire broke through. Dad jumped off the tractor seat and fell onto the ice. He stood up, stumbled, and slid to the pond's edge just as the ice gave way and the tractor began to sink. Not only was he very stubborn, he was not real bright. And his love of baseball never wavered.

The Dayton Ducks are by far the most well-known and remembered team in Dayton baseball history. The coach of the Ducks wanted to recruit Dad to come play for the league, but, by law, the team had to wait until he was eighteen years of age. Unfortunately, the team folded when World War II began. Dad never got his chance to become a major league baseball player, so he reverted to Plan B. He joined the military.

To escape the poverty in which he lived, Clancy lied about his age, joining the Marine Corps in 1942 when he was seventeen years old, at the start of World War II. My dad was assigned to the 2nd Marine Division. He completed boot camp training and was promptly put on a ship headed to the South Pacific. His brother, Leroy, had joined the Marine Corps several years earlier and was assigned to the 3rd Marine Division. Leroy was fighting in the Solomon Islands. Leroy was awarded the Silver Star for his bravery during the fierce battle of Bougainville. Uncle Leroy came home from World War II a hero only to lose his life years later to colon cancer. A death that he could have easily prevented had he not refused to have a colonoscopy. The brothers shared a family trait. Stubbornness.

Dad served his country proudly, fighting in the fierce battles of Guadalcanal and Iwo Jima. He rarely spoke of his experiences. He kept his memories of World War II in a file folder with the drawer firmly shut. After the war, he attended college on the G.I. Bill at Ohio State University. Clancy obtained a civil engineering degree. After a short stint working for Lockheed Martin, he set off on his own to start Industrial Building Products, i.e. "the Company" in 1952.

My grandfather died shortly after Dad left for the war. He tripped and fell on the front stairs of their small house in Cuyahoga Falls. The same stairs my dad was to fix but never did because he was at baseball practice. Clancy's dad died from complications due to his fall.

# Nine
## Lost

Like most small towns in the 1970s, families in Clarkston generally belong to a church and attend Sunday services. We attended Mass at St. Daniel's Catholic Church every Sunday. When you attend church in a small town regularly, you notice that families tend to sit in the same spots.

The Freitags sat with their seven children in a pew two rows in front of us. While Patrick and I would fidget during Mass, the red headed twins, Doreen and Danny, never made a move. Not even a glance our way. Not a fidget. I am sure there would've been hell to pay if they did. No one ever really knows what goes on behind closed doors, but I suspect those kids took a real whooping if they stepped out of line. I went to Catechism with the twins. Every once in a while, I would catch a glimpse of fear in Doreen or Danny's eyes. That same fear the nice neighbor lady had in hers. I don't know for sure if there was abuse going on in the house they were raised in.

Doreen and Danny were both in my second grade class. Our classroom was engrossed in one of the most enjoyable projects of elementary school I can remember. Michigan Week. Or maybe it was Michigan Weeks. The perception of time is much different when you are a child than when you're an adult. The junior high woodshop classes made us elementary students plywood covers for the Michigan books we made. There were several designs from which to choose, all of them our state symbols. I had difficulty choosing between the apple blossom and the robin, but the apple blossom eventually won. Almost all the boys chose the trout.

The students in each classroom spent several days studying the native Michigan Indians. One class made a large wigwam from branches, twine, and painted sheets. Another class made a model of Ft. Pontchartrain. Someone had loaned the school a large painting of Chief Pontiac. Our school principal displayed it proudly in the school hallway.

That same year Mom, worried about my frequent night terrors, made an appointment for me to see our local doctor. I hated going to Doctor O'Neill's office. It was always jam-packed with sick kids. It seemed to take forever too. I tried to entertain myself during the long wait in the crowded waiting room reading outdated copies of *Scholastic Magazine*.

"How much longer?" I whined.

The door that separated the waiting room and the exam rooms opened again. *Please let it be my turn. I cannot endure one more minute with these whiny toddlers.* A big woman dressed in white shirt, white pants, and white shoes looked down at a chart. The anticipation was killing me. Finally she announced, "Ann Johns." I tossed the *Scholastic Magazine* onto the coffee table and walked toward the big woman. Holding a stack of patient charts and blocking the door, she glared at me. Almost as if challenging me to a game of Red Rover. Mom quickly gathered her purse and jacket and joined us.

The big woman held the door for us then turned and started walking down the hallway. She showed us into the exam room on the left.

"The doctor will be with you shortly."

The exam room door shut leaving Mom and me alone in the room to endure more waiting.

"Has she been under an extended period of stress?" Dr. O'Neill asked.

"Not that I am aware of," Mom answered.

"Stress that causes the kind of night terrors you describe isn't from just a few days of tension. Stress that causes actual night terrors is usually caused by life transitions," Dr. O'Neill continued, still addressing my mother.

*Why is it adults talk about children as if they are a third person and not even in the room?* I wanted to scream at them both: *Life transitions! How about all the death in this town since we moved here? Maybe that is what is causing my nightmares.*

"You should try to reduce the pressures that may be causing the night terrors. Does she have any unusual fears or is it just the night terrors?" the doctor asked.

"She has anxiety about the dangers of swimming, boating, biking, and riding in a car."

"Do you know when it started?"

"I think it started when she witnessed Mr. and Mrs. Lee being hit by a train. We were two cars behind the Lees on White Lake Road when the train struck their car. Could that be the cause of her anxiety?"[1]

Dr. O'Neill started rambling on with some medical jargon. My mind flashed back to that day. There was no indication that a train was even coming. I could always hear a train coming, but not that day. It all happened so fast. The train actually pushed the Lee's car thirty-five feet down the tracks.

"That could certainly play a part in it, Mrs. Johns."

*Maybe it has something to do with the freak accidents around here*, I thought. Just the week before, Mr. Smith's neighbor found him lying dead in the snow.[2] Undersheriff Hazen said it appeared that the tree he was attempting to bulldoze down lashed back.

"I will prescribe her something to help her sleep. Let's see if that helps," Dr. O'Neill said pulling a prescription pad out of his white lab coat pocket. "Come back in a month, and let's see how she's doing."

Mom made me take the medicine every night before bed that Dr. O'Neill prescribed. I didn't like taking it. The medicine made it hard for me to wake up in the morning. The medication seemed to help the night terrors at first, but just a few weeks later, they were back. The night terrors started the night I read an article in the paper about the death of eighteen-year-old Larry Worley.[3] The paper reported that Larry died while working at his job at Price Brothers on White Lake Road. Somehow a front-end loader full of cement just fell on him. It was like a punch to the gut when I read the article. I didn't even know Larry Worley, but something about the accident must have stuck in my subconscious, causing the night terrors to return.

Consciousness was just out of reach. I struggled to wake up and escape the dream. There were big trucks lined up outside our house ready to destroy it with me inside. The trucks started moving closer. They were almost to the house. *It's just a dream. It's just a dream.* My eyelids were so heavy. I struggled to wake. *Wake up! Wake up! Wake up!* I sat up in bed and took a few deep breathes. Beads of sweat tickled my temples, eventually making their way down my face. I took deep breaths in through my nose and out of my mouth trying to slow my heart rate. When I finally had my wits about me, I pulled back the bed covers and slid out of bed.

"Hey, Mom," I said as I sauntered into the kitchen groggy from fitful sleep. I didn't notice that Mom was on the phone. She didn't like it when I interrupted her telephone conversations, so I tried to avoid doing it. If I interrupted her, she would give me the I-raised-you-to-have-some-manners lecture after she hung up.

"Lynn, I am telling you, I wasn't in town this morning! I don't know whose car you put those baby squirrels in, but I can assure you, it wasn't mine. Someone is going to get a nice surprise when they open their back-seat door!" Mom was laughing so hard tears were streaming down her face. My mother's laugh is contagious. I started giggling just listening to her. Mom hung up the telephone, turned, and smiled at me.

"How did you sleep, dear?"

"With my eyes shut," I responded sarcastically.

"Don't be a sassy pants, Annie."

"Squirrels?"

"Mrs. Casey found a nest of five baby squirrels in her attic. She was on her way to the animal shelter to drop them off. She saw my station wagon parked downtown and thought you might like to try to take care of them. So, deciding we should raise the baby squirrels, she pulled over and put the box of squirrels in the back seat of my car. The only problem is, it wasn't my car!"

Mom started laughing again. I started laughing too. That was classic!

"You got up just in time, sweetie."

"What's up? Please don't tell me the farrier is coming today, Mom."

"No farrier today. Your grandpa called. He wants to go out to Gulick Lake and see how the fish are biting. He needs an extra set of hands getting the boat into the water, so I told him you were available. So, it's a good thing you're up. He should be here in less than a half an hour." Mom set a glass of orange juice down in front of me.

"I hope the fish are biting! I am going to bring any fish I catch back here and put them in the pond." After downing the orange juice in just a few gulps, I skipped out of the kitchen and headed toward the basement to gather my fishing gear.

I flipped on the basement light switch and descended the stairs. Smokey's gold eyes shined from under the workbench. Smokey was getting so old. He was spending more and more time away from us and in the basement. I was sure the end of his life was near. I chose not to think about it.

"Hey, big guy," I greeted the old cat. He responded by rubbing the side of his face against my leg. I grabbed my fishing pole and tackle box and bounded back up the stairs two at a time.

Gulick Lake used to be a pretty big lake, about eighteen acres, before it shrank into virtual swamp land. Even before it shrank, the lake was shallow, maybe eight feet deep. Grandpa and I were making small talk as he drove. Both of us excited to catch some fish. We arrived at Gulick Lake to find emergency vehicles parked along the shore. Grandpa pulled his car up behind a police vehicle and turned off the engine. Neither one of us spoke. A sheriff's deputy walked up and approached the driver's side window. Grandpa cranked his window down. "Afternoon," Grandpa greeted the officer.

"Hey, John. Nice to see you," the deputy said tipping his hat.

"Something wrong?"

"No fishing today, John. Sadly, there's been a drowning."[4]

"Sorry to hear that, Ted. Anything I can do to help?"

"Thanks for the offer. We're all set. Just waiting for the county coroner to show up. You can come back in a couple of hours if you want. Give my best to Ruth."

"Will do."

Grandpa rolled up the car window and placed his hand on my knee. I looked down at the familiar hand. There was something calming, steading really, about Grandpa's touch.

"You okay?" he asked me. The look of concern was evident on his face.

I just nodded affirmatively. *Another drowning. I pray it is not one of my friends.*

"Since we can't fish, how about we drive out to Cook's Farm and get an ice cream?"

"Sounds good, Grandpa."

Traveling down Sashabaw Road, I gazed out the window, lost in my thoughts. We passed Pine Knob Music Theatre and the Pierre's Farm Market. After that, there was nothing else but trees really until we reached Seymour Lake Road. My grandparents were aware of my recent anxiety issues. Grandma thought food fixed everything. That's probably why Grandpa threw out the ice cream invitation. I didn't feel like having an ice cream, but I would never hurt Grandpa's feelings by refusing the treat. He turned on his left blinker signaling our turn into Cooks Farm Dairy.

Turns out it was John Abbott who drown in Gulick Lake that day.[4] John was a tenth grader who was active on the track and debate teams at Clarkston High School. John and some friends had gone to Gulick Lake for a swim. John's friends told the authorities that John disappeared just after they went into the water. John's body was recovered, lifeless, in six feet of water. A sadness shrouded the town when John died. That sadness would last the entire summer.

The summer of 1971 was the hottest on record since the Detroit riots. I knew it was hot when Mom chose to spend the day at Walter's Lake rather than horseback riding. While Dad was at work, Mom, Patrick, and I tried to beat the heat by floating in the cool waters of the lake.

"Whew, it is another hot one," Grandma said looking at the thermometer that read ninety-nine degrees. We had endured weeks of temperatures near or above one hundred degrees. The grass was dying and dogs were digging holes under porches in an attempt to beat the heat. I was in Grandma's tiny kitchen helping peel potatoes when Grandpa came through the front door. He and some other men had formed a search party trying to find a local handyman who had gone missing.[5]

"Any signs of him, John?"

"No sign yet, Ruth."

"It just doesn't make any sense. Clarkston is a small village. Where could he have possibly wandered off too?"

"Do you think someone kidnapped him?" I asked.

"Now what would someone want with an old man, Annie? Mr. Muchler probably just got himself turned around. We'll find him," Grandpa said as he reached in the refrigerator for a cold beer.

*Two weeks is a long time to get yourself turned around in the woods,* I thought. *I could walk from here to Ohio in two weeks. Unless I was walking in circles.*

The missing handyman was Lee Muchler. He was a polite, gray-haired man who'd pumped our gas at Morgan's gas station. He sometimes did odd jobs for Mom at our house. He did odd jobs for some of my friends parents too. Mr. Muchler had been missing for almost two weeks. Lots of folks were really worried about him.

The mystery of missing Mr. Muchler started when police found his car abandoned along the side of the road. Search parties found no sign of him. Sadly, the mystery was solved when Michigan State Police found Mr. Muchler's dehydrated, starved, and emaciated body in a local park. His body was found in almost the exact same spot Grandpa had searched just the day before. Along with his body, the police found a Clarkston Library card and a note that said, *no food in fourteen days.* Mr. Muchler was born in 1906. He died alone in the woods in 1971. Perhaps the searing heat scorched Mr. Muchler's brain, rendering him incapable of making sense of where he was. My grandparents attended the funeral. Grandma took a pie.

# Ten
# Seabiscuit

The Michigan State Fairgrounds opened in 1858 on twenty acres in Detroit on the west side of Woodward Avenue. The fairgrounds were just far enough from Detroit's city center to make it a pleasant walk. By 1913, the state fair's program expanded to include a Detroit Symphony Orchestra concert, a cow milking contest, vaudeville shows, a husband-calling competition, and the auction of two steers by the governor.[1] Expansions over the years added to the grounds a cattle barn, poultry building, a coliseum, band shell, and a grandstand. In 1951, Cunningham's Drug Stores provided two trains and offered free rides. By the 1960s, the fair drew families from all over the Midwest. Attendance grew into the millions over the two-week period. Back then, the concerts and exhibits were free. The only thing that cost any money were rides and food, and even those were reasonable. The fair was affordable, so families would go several times during the two-week event.

After purchasing our tickets at the gate, we proceeded to the former home of the eighteenth President of the United States, Ulysses S. Grant. Once we got that over with, Mom took us to the horse track and told us *again* how Grandpa was there on September 7, 1936 when, before a crowd of 28,000 people, Seabiscuit won his very first race, The Governor's Handicap Race.[2] It was the fiftieth race of the horse's career. Seabiscuit and his jockey, Red Pollard, repeated the feat on September 26, 1936 at the fairgrounds, winning the Hendrie Handicap. This incredible racehorse quickly became a national hero due in part to his accomplishment at the Detroit Fairgrounds. In 1938, Seabiscuit was named Horse of the Year. In 1958, Seabiscuit was voted into the National Museum of Racing Hall of Fame. Mom's favorite thing to see at the fair were the horses. The best part of the Michigan State Fair was the barn animal barns if you asked me.[3]

I love animals. It doesn't matter what kind of animal it is; I love them all. Because we lived on a farm, Mom and Dad didn't object much when I brought home a stray animal. Besides the occasional barn kitten, I brought home rabbits, chickens, a duckling, and even a litter of baby raccoons once. But the duckling turned out to be the most problematic.

We named the duckling Benny. Benny lived in my bathroom until he got big enough to stay outside. When he was big enough, and it was safe to move him outdoors, I made a nice nest in a cardboard box for him on the back porch. For whatever reason, Benny decided Mom, not me, was his mother, so he followed her everywhere. And mom's horse, Randy, hated that duck. If Benny came anywhere near the barn, Randy would flatten his ears back, bare his teeth, and go after him. If Benny saw Mom, he would follow her. And since Benny wanted to follow Mom anywhere and everywhere, she had to sneak out to the barn to keep the poor duck from following and getting hurt by the horse. If Benny hadn't flown south for the winter with the other wild ducks, I think Mom would have made duck soup out of him.


"There are lots of good performances scheduled at the fair this year, Patsy," Dad said flipping through the Sunday paper.

"Who's playing?" she asked.

"Glen Campbell, The Platters, Tom Jones, The 5th Dimension, and The Jackson 5."

"The Jackson 5, really?" I asked as I grabbed for the paper. "Can we go?"

"We'll see," was my mother's non-committal response.

Days of pestering my parents to see The Jackson 5 perform at the fair fell on deaf ears. Mom's entertainment choice trumped mine. Instead of seeing Michael Jackson and The Jackson 5, we saw Tom Jones.[4] Not exactly a kid's first choice of entertainment.


I disliked my parents' choice of concerts just as much as I disliked my parents' choice of television programs. We only had one television, and shows were limited, so if I wanted to watch television, I had to watch what my parents were watching. I could usually talk Patrick into playing a game of checkers with me if our parents were watching a television show we didn't like. The only thing worse than watching a television show we didn't like was when Mom and Dad made us watch the news. Our parents felt it was important for us to be educated about what was happening in the world. There was an advertisement during the news one night about an invention that allowed you to turn a television into a game. The invention was called *Pong*.

Our parents got Patrick and me *Pong* for Christmas that year. Clarkston hosted its first Winter Carnival that year too. The carnival was held in February, just a few days after my birthday. I signed up to compete in the ice skating race on Mill Pond, but I didn't win. I didn't even finish in the top twenty. The school class that created the best ice sculpture was awarded a traveling trophy. I can't remember which class won. The Boy Scouts held a dog sledding exhibition. There were hockey, figure skating, and ice fishing competitions. There was a winter queen contest too.

Our small town was beginning to grow, and I was enjoying its new activities.

Winter Carnival was the highlight of the season for me. Drugs were the highlight of the season for many of the older kids. The parking lot on Main Street became a hotbed for drug traffic. Michigan State Police spotted a suspicious vehicle on Allen Road just down the street from our house. The police raided the house and seized over 640 pounds of marijuana.[5] County police made over three hundred arrests for narcotics that year.[6] And it didn't take long for the drug problem to spread from the parking lot on Main Street to the high school and then to the junior high school. Two of my friends would overdose that year, one on PCP at her home and one on acid during science class. Luckily, both of them survived.

After checking the paper for any reference to the most recent school drug overdose incident, I proceeded to look for the school's weekly lunch menu. A typical school week menu went something like this: hamburger gravy on mashed potatoes on Monday, baked beans and franks on Tuesday, meat loaf on Wednesday, Thursday was almost always toasted cheese sandwich and tomato soup, and Friday was usually fish sticks. As I was flipping through the newspaper pages, an article caught my eye: "Killed in crash."[7] Mike Seymour, age twenty-two, died in a small plane crash on April 18th, the article stated. *Another young Clarkston person dead. How sad. Grandma will see this article and tell Grandpa how she was right to make him sell his airplane.*

My grandfather was a very safe pilot. He had what he called his pilot tricks. One of his tricks was to place a glass half full of water on the dashboard of his plane. When I asked him why he flew with a half a glass of water, he told me it was his "dumpy level."

He explained that if he ever lost his orientation in fog, he could always keep the plane level by keeping the water in the glass level. I don't know if Mike Seymour's crash was the result of fog or not. It didn't really matter what caused the crash. It didn't really matter if Mike was in a plane, train, or automobile. If the evil that fell on our village wanted you, it was going to get you.

*Maybe Grandma is right. All any one could do is pray.* I slowly closed the paper and made a mental note to pack my lunch. Groceries were usually scarce in our house by Friday. After searching the kitchen cupboards for something to pack, I settled on a peanut butter and jelly sandwich made from two butts of a loaf of bread. I put my sandwich in a baggie and set it on the kitchen counter closest to the back door so I wouldn't forget it in the morning.

The school day dragged, but it finally ended. I was fortunate to have scored a seat by myself on the school bus. *TGIF.* It had been raining all day, which didn't help my gray mood. Bus 32 slowed as it neared my stop. I stood up, grabbed my backpack, and headed to the front of the bus. The doors parted to open. I trotted down the three steps to the dirt road. Bus 32 pulled away, its large tires splattering mud onto my white Ked shoes. I looked down at my shoes, looked up at the gray sky, and headed down the soggy dirt road toward home. *Crayola should make a crayon color called Michigan Gray.*

I slammed the back door, dropped my backpack on the floor, took off my jean jacket, and tossed it in the general direction of my backpack. I stomped up the stairs and slammed my bedroom door. *School sucks.*

A few minutes later there was a soft knock on my door. I ignored it. The knock intensified. I ignored it. Mom cracked the door open.

"Rough day?"

"School is so boring."

"Can I come in?"

I scooched over so she could sit on the side of my bed.

"One of Mrs. Cook's mares is in labor, and she asked me to come help with the delivery. I'll be heading over there after I feed tonight. Wanna come?"

"Why not. I've got nothing better to do."

Mrs. Cook was one of Mom's best friends. My dad didn't like her. He considered her a bad influence on my mother. Dad said it wasn't just because Mrs. Cook was a divorcee that made her a bad influence. He said she smoked too much, drank too much (if that isn't the pot calling the kettle black), and cursed too much. Dad referred to her as "the loud mouth broad."

The Cook farm was just a few miles from our house, down on Davisburg Road. The farm's barn was amazing. It had fourteen stalls, ten horses, and lots of barn cats. Mrs. Cook kept that barn as neat as a pin. The best thing about visiting her farm was the barn cats. In the spring, there was always a mess of kittens. Mrs. Cook had a slight build, short hair, and deep brown eyes. Her voice was raspy and hoarse, probably from too much smoking. Besides the smoking, she probably spent too much time outside. Her skin was as tough as leather. And I adored her. Mrs. Cook had a fun, energetic personality. The best thing about her was her sarcastic, inappropriate sense of humor. Leave it to her to say what others were thinking but dared not say.

It was still raining when we arrived at the farm. Mom and I sloshed through the mud, bypassed the house, and headed straight toward the barn. Light shined through the bottom of the large barn door. I dug my left foot into the ground and pushed the door open to the right. The familiar aroma of horse manure mixed with grain and damp hay hit my nostrils. Mrs. Cook was standing outside the mare's stall door.

"She is really struggling, Pat."

Mom and I watched the mare circling around her stall. Mom slid open the stall door and went inside. The mare greeted her with a toss of her strong head and a low whinny.

"Whoa, girl. It's going to be okay," Mom addressed the mare, gently running her hands down the animal's mane and across her back. She moved her hands down the mare's side and under her belly. She reached for its halter, gently moving the horse's head over to her right shoulder so she would slide to the mare's left side.

Mrs. Cook and I watched Mom assess the mare's condition. My mother has a special way with horses. It is almost as if she can communicate with them through her hands. "I need some rubber gloves, Doris."

"I'll get 'em." I ran toward the tack room.

"Second shelf on the right," Mrs. Cook hollered after me.

I flipped the switch to turn on the tack room light. I glanced around the room. Two cats were curled up on top of a saddle. They both lifted their sleepy heads and looked in my direction. I spotted the gloves, grabbed them, and ran back.

Mom slipped on the long rubber gloves, lifted the mare's tail, and inserted her right hand into the mare.

"The foul is breach, Doris. I need your help."

Mrs. Cook joined my mother in the stall. Mom gave instruction as she manipulated the foul's position inside the mare's womb. I pulled over a few bails of straw to sit on and settled in. The two women worked on that mare for hours and hours. Oddly, the mare didn't seem to mind. Finally, just past 1:00 am, a beautiful filly was born. And she was a beauty.

"Good morning." I greeted Mom as I strolled into the kitchen, famished and looking for something to eat. It had been a long night and we hadn't eaten dinner.

"Good morning, Annie," Mom responded exhaling smoke from a cigarette.

"Watching that filly being born last night was the coolest thing ever!"

"Glad you appreciated it, Annie. Kids these days don't always appreciate God's miracles."

"That truly was amazing! Has Mrs. Cook picked out a name for her yet?"

"Not yet. Any suggestions?"

I thought for a minute. "Patience," I announced.

Mom laughed. "Patience. I like it!"

"Speaking of Mrs. Cook, she is stopping by to help me with the farrier in a bit. Then we're going to drive out to Metamora to look at a saddle. "Would you like to ride along?"

I poured some Captain Crunch cereal into a bowl.

"No thanks. Sarah wants me to go riding, and Nancy wants me to babysit with her. What's the weather supposed to be?" I asked.

"Hot and sticky with storms later."

"In that case, I think I will ride my bike over to Nancy's and go babysit with her."

"Who and where is she babysitting?"

"Some little boy over on Ellis Road. I think his name is Eric."

Mom flinched. Just a very slight flinch. I don't think most folks would have even noticed. But I noticed. I did the math and then felt bad for saying the boy's name. He was about the age my little brother would have been had he not died.

It would be just a few weeks later that five-year-old Eric Booth would drown in Otter Lake during a family outing.[8]

*I was right on my brother's heels as he ran down our grandparent's dock. Patrick cannonballed into the lake, and I jumped in right behind him. The water was cool on my sweaty skin. I started to paddle toward the surface. I could see the sunlight dancing on the water just a few feet above. Only a few more strokes and I will be on the surface, I thought. I kicked my feet and continued toward the surface of the water. But the surface wasn't getting any closer. I swam harder. The surface still wasn't getting any closer. I could feel my lungs start to burn. I needed air. I was starting to panic. I am going to drown. Oh God, I am going to drown.*

Opening my eyes, I shot straight up in bed, gasping for air. I was having that same nightmare over and over. I laid back down. Smokey was asleep at the foot of my bed, undisturbed. I rolled over onto my right side and pulled the covers up to my chin. The breeze coming through my bedroom window was considerably cooler than it was when I fell asleep. I lay there contemplating getting out of bed and shutting the windows, but fell back to sleep before I decided.

"Annie, are you up?" Mom yelled up the stairs.

I ignored her, pulling the covers over my head.

"Annie?" she yelled again.

"What?" I yelled back.

"We are leaving for church in half an hour. Get up and get dressed."

As usual, our parents were bickering as we piled into the car and headed to St. Dan's. We arrived just before the entrance hymn started. The Freitags were selected to bring up the gifts before communion. *Better them than us.* I didn't like it when our family was selected to take the gifts up to the alter. It was inevitable. Our village was small and our parish was small. So each family got selected a few times a year. And when you were selected, everyone in church stared while you carried the communion gifts from the back of the church to the alter. I was always petrified of that walk,

79

convinced I was going to trip and spill the communion host all over the floor.

"Let us pray for the souls of Timothy and Steve, the two young boys who were called to the right side of the Father much too soon, their young lives lost at the hand of their mother."[9] My fellow parishioners bowed their heads in prayer. I leaned in towards Mom to ask her who Timothy and Steve were, but I stopped as the priest's sermon got louder. "What evil could cause a mother to take the lives of her sons by her own hand?" Father Weingartz asked the parishioners rhetorically. I attempted to whisper my question to Mom again, but the priest continued. "In John's Gospel, Jesus enlists the help of Saint Michael the Archangel. Saint Michael, defend us in battle, be our protection against the wickedness and snares of the devil. Oh Prince of the Heavenly Host, by the divine power of God, cast into hell Satan and all the evil spirits who roam throughout the world seeking the ruin of souls."

Once again, I leaned in toward Mom to ask her who Timothy and Steve were. "Mom."

She leaned toward me. "What is it?" she asked impatiently.

Before I could answer her, Father Weingartz started again. "Each of us have our own battles against the devil who is trying to turn us away from eternal life with our Creator. Satan's idea for our eternal life is one spent with him in hatred and misery. Satan was able to turn Sandra Hausker away from our Creator and into an eternal life of misery when he tempted her to murder her two young sons, Timothy, age six; and Steve, age three. Let us pray for her and the souls of her two young boys." Mom took the quick moment of silence to see what I was pestering her about.

"What is so important you need to interrupt Father Weinzgartz's prayer?" she whispered.

"Never mind," I whispered back.

Mom nudged me to stand up. I was lost in my own thoughts

about the boys who were killed by their own mother. *Mothers are supposed to protect their children. This wasn't an accident like it was when Jerry Warren got killed. The police were saying it was his Dad's fault though. Maybe it was an accident or maybe something evil took over his Dad's mind making him try to pass another car causing the accident that threw nine-year-old Jerry from the car and killed him.[10] It was for sure something evil that made Mrs. Hausker kill her boys though.*

My fellow parishioners were reciting the Apostle's Creed. Mom had been helping me memorize the profession of faith, one of my Catechism assignments. I wasn't joining in. I wasn't trying to be defiant or anything, my mind just couldn't remember any of the words. Mom shot me one of her looks. My mind kept drifting back to those two little boys. I found it extremely difficult to concentrate through the rest of Mass. I got a lecture on the way home.

A can of hairspray in her left hand and a hair pick in the right, mom was putting finishing touches on her hair. She was wearing a black skirt and a white blouse. The feet on the end of her long, sleek legs plunged into a pair of high-heel, black, open-toe shoes. A small pearl necklace lay softly around her long, thin neck.

"There are some pot pies in the freezer for you and your brother. We should be home before nine. If there is an emergency, call your grandparents."

Mom spent most of her time in the barn, so it was a rare occasion for her to wear makeup. When she did get dressed up to go somewhere, somewhere that made her feel like she should wear makeup, I would sit on the bathroom counter and put some on too. Mom was concentrating on applying eye shadow.

"Are you taking a pie to the funeral home?" I asked putting the cap back on her lipstick.

"Feeding people when they are sad is something your grand-mother does."

"Why does she do that?"

Mom set the eyeshadow down on the counter. She was being very thoughtful about her answer.

"Mom? Why does Grandma always take a pie?"

She turned and looked at me. Her light blue eyes beaming with love and with a dab of concern too.

"Maybe your grandmother thinks feeding people will make them feel better, fill that empty space in their heart I guess. Your grandmother wants to show she cares, and that's how she does it."

"I don't think eating pie is going to help fill the empty space David and Brian's parents are feeling, Mom."

"I don't think so either, sweetheart."

My parents were going to give their condolences to the parents of one of Patrick's best friends. Norm's brother was killed in a car accident. Brian Evely was seventeen when he died instantly in a head-on collision on a local road.[11, 12] His passenger, David Young, was just thirteen years old when the two boys died.

Brian's thirteen year old brother, Norm, survived his injuries when his bike got hit by a car just a year later.[13] God had a hand in that. Sparing those parents the loss of two sons.

Needing some fresh air to clear my head, I went outside and hopped on my bike. I didn't tell Patrick where I was going, not that he cared. Heck, I didn't even know where I was going. I turned south on Allen Road and peddled in the direction of town. It was early spring and the dirt road was a muddy mess. The tires on my bike were flinging mud up onto my shoes and pants. The faster I peddled the higher up the mud landed on my pant legs. I was never bothered by a little mud. The cool air was exhilarating.

After conquering the three hills on Allen Road, I turned right on Holcomb Street. I peddled as fast as my young muscles would go on the flat stretch of road. I arrived at the Miller Farm in short order. I loved the Miller Farm. It was one of my favorite spots around.

In spring of 1837, George Miller traveled in a covered wagon on some tough dirt roads to Clarkston from New York. Mrs. Miller and the children arrived later by freight barge to the dirt streets of Detroit, which bustled with French Canadian Fur Traders, Indians, and busy shops.[14] Upon arriving to Clarkston, the Miller brood of children was a bit shocked to find their neighbors were Indians. The eldest son, Sam, told stories about growing up with the Indian boys. I looked across the 300 acres of rich pasture filled with cattle to the woods edge. Sam had said he remembered the large packs of wolves that once roamed those woods. They would try to get into the barn to eat the chickens and pigs, he'd said.

My attention turned to the grand house that stood just off Bridge Lake Road. Sam, like his father, had loved to farm. He'd acquired this acreage for his own farm and built the nineteen-room home in 1877. I was dying to go inside.[15] Grandma had said she would be happy to take me over and introduce me to the present-day Mrs. Miller. I never did take her up on that offer. Partly because I was shy and partly because I had a picture in my mind of what the house looked like inside, and I didn't want to spoil it.

Sadly, Sam Miller died not long after my visit. He was cutting hay when the tractor he was riding hit a stump.[16] The impact threw him off of his tractor and into the path of the mower. Today, most of the Miller Farm acreage has been sold off to make way for "progress," but Sam's house and barn still stand.

# Eleven
# Death to Deer Lake

Deer Lake is the gem of Clarkston. The lake is fed by the waters of the Clinton River, which runs for 760 miles.[1] Grandpa said the river was renamed in honor of DeWitt Clinton, the governor of New York in the 1800s. Previously, the river's name was Nottawasippee, which the Native Americans gave it. The word "Nottawasippee" means "like rattlesnakes." I think Nottawasippee was a much more suitable name for the lake.

Mr. Meyland took a rattlesnake he found in a neighbor's drive near Cranberry Lake to the Detroit Zoo rather than killing it. Zoo officials told Mr. Meyland that Clarkston is the Massasauga rattler capital of Michigan.[2,3] Sadie got herself bit on the nose by a rattler on more than one occasion. Poor dog's nose would swell up something awful. My friend Sarah lived a few miles down Allen Road. She got bit once too. Mrs. Parker's dog cornered a rattler in her driveway. Luckily, Mrs. Yantiss ran over it with a hoe and chopped the snake's head off before it bit Mrs. Parker's dog. Mike Herron was out catching frogs with his little brother, Donnie in the pond behind their house when he stepped on a rattler. Donnie grabbed a stick and killed the snake but not before the snake bit Mike. Mike spent five days in the hospital and got thirty-seven injections. Mike's experience pretty much made me scared to death of snakes. The Massassauga rattler likes water, so I was always extra watchful around the tall grass close to the lake's shore.[4]

Deer Lake is about a mile long and over a mile wide. The lake encompasses 137 acres and is over sixty feet deep in some parts. Deer Lake is spring fed, beautiful, pure, and cold. Grandpa said the lake was at one time the center of a thriving summer colony. There used to be two hotels located on its banks: the Deer Lake Inn and the Green Acres Inn.

Grandpa often took me fishing there. He would tell me stories about the visitors who rode the train from Detroit to Pontiac and then traveled by horse and buggy to Clarkston. In 1883, the population of Clarkston was four hundred; in 1973, it had grown to one thousand; and today, it is over thirty thousand.[5] Long before the lake was swarming with speedboats and jet skis, it was swarming with fish. We grew up swimming, fishing, and canoeing on the tranquil waters of Deer Lake. A developer wanted to build a huge housing development on the lake and lots of folks were against it, Grandpa included.

"I cannot believe the township would even consider allowing a city neighborhood, or as they call it, "a subdivision," to take over the entire north side of the lake!" Grandpa's anger was clear to all of us sitting at the dinner table. He almost slammed, rather than set his fork down on the table. His strong German features were stern, and his face was red. His eyes looked dark behind his metal-framed glasses.

My mother opened her mouth to say something. Grandma gave her a stern look. "Don't get him started," she said.

"If folks want city living, they should just stay in the city!" His rant continued. "We are going to see incidents like the one we had last weekend. Poor boys could have been killed by that reckless boater!"

Grandpa was referring to Tom Pidd and his friend Seil. They

were canoeing when a pontoon boat pulling a skier rammed right into the canoe the boys were in despite the fact the boys stood up and were screaming and hollering and waving their arms at the driver. The boys could've been killed if they hadn't dived for their lives right before the pontoon hit their canoe smashing it to pieces.[6]

I don't think I had ever before, or ever since, seen Grandpa so angry about anything as he was about that housing development. He attended every town meeting and called every influential person in town to try to stop "progress."

The proposed housing development was to be located on hundreds of acres behind St. Daniel's Catholic Church. I understood and shared Grandpa's concern. Patrick and I spent countless hours exploring and digging for treasures on that land while Grandpa fished. If we got real lucky, we would find an Indian arrowhead. Patrick had found several and kept them in a small wooden box in his bedroom. Grandpa and his friends fished the lake in the summer and hunted the fields in the fall to provide food for their families. There was something mystical about the land surrounding Deer Lake. I could sit in the fields for hours just watching the tops of the long grass dance in the wind, moving gracefully from side to side as though choreographed to represent a native dance. If you listened closely, the blades of grass made a soft sound as they touched one another. City folks would say that grass can't make music, but I would tell you it can.

After a fierce battle, the township board members approved a fifteen-hundred home subdivision to be built on the vacant land along the lake's pristine north shores. Progress had come to Clarkston. Grandpa couldn't believe the township members actually approved it. He was heartbroken. Devastated really.

Grandpa parked high up on a hunting trail overlooking Deer Lake. The smoke from his Lucky Strike cigarette stung my nostrils as it drifted past my face and out the passenger car window.

"Michigan's waters were very important to the Indians who lived here."

Based on the look on Grandpa's face and the tone of his voice, I knew that one of his stories was coming.

"Native Americans were great woodworkers," Grandpa continued. "They made birch bark canoes and traveled along our lakes and rivers long before the white man came. The trails they made became the routes the first settlers used. Dixie Highway actually started as an Indian trail. Along the Indian trails, archeologists have found over two hundred-sixty burial grounds."[7]

Grandpa paused. I turned and looked at him. He took in another long draw on his cigarette and exhaled, never looking at me. He was lost in his own thoughts. I studied his face. My grandfather, John Joseph Tisch, was a man of average height with a strong, sturdy build. Some might say he was stocky. His nose was a bit too large for his face. A thick white mustache sat right above his mouth, which was normally turned up in a smile. On that day, his mouth was turned down as if defeated. Grandpa continued.

"One of the largest burial grounds was found on the Rouge River. I've heard that it was actually a mound forty feet high and several hundred feet long. Can you imagine that, Annie? I read an article once, back in the 1950s, long before you were born, that a local Indian woman warned that it's not good to disturb the place where people are buried. She warned that the Yam-Ko-Desh still roam there."[8]

Grandpa and I sat there in silence looking down at the pristine waters. Many of the trees were already gone. Bulldozers and excavators, now abandoned and quiet, were scattered over several acres. Grandpa crushed out his cigarette in the ashtray. I finally spoke.

"What are Yam-Ko-Desh?" I asked.

"As I understand it, the Yam-Ko-Desh are the spirits of people buried in the land."

"Do you think people are buried on this land Grandpa?"

"I don't know if anyone really knows for sure. But to unearth this land is a bad idea. Some things man should not disturb. For a lot of reasons, Annie."

Grandpa fired up the truck. "I better get you back to the house."

Grandpa and I returned from Rudy's with the few items Grandma had sent us to fetch.

"What on earth took you two so long?" Grandma asked.

"We stopped at the lake for a spell," Grandpa sighed. "I just can't believe it, Ruth. It is the responsibility of the entire community to take care of our lakes, Ruth. For our children's sake if for no other reason."

I left my grandparents to their conversation and joined Mom on the porch. Patrick was throwing sticks for Velvet in the yard.

"Why would anyone shoot that sweet man?" Mom mumbled to no one in particular.

"Who got shot, Mom?"

"Mr. Diericks."

She was reading the paper and sipping on a cup of coffee. Mr. Diericks lived just off of Main Street with his family. Like so many other folks in our village, Mr. Diericks spent most of his life working at the same job in the automotive industry. He had dedicated over thirty years of his life to working for the Pontiac Motor Company.

Grandma hollered from the kitchen, "Mr. Diericks got shot?"

I swear Grandma had the ears of a hawk. She joined us on the porch a few moments later.

"Someone just shot him in the head. Paper says it wasn't robbery, and the sheriff can't find a motive. Pure evil is the only explanation for such a senseless killing."[9]

"God is always in control, Patricia, so God would've had to give permission for this evil. So, evil is hardly the explanation."

"Spoken like the true Irish Catholic that you are, Mother."

"Why would God give permission for evil to come and hurt Mr. Diericks?" I asked.

"So, his family, friends, and neighbors might turn to God in prayer with a renewed trust in His love and concern for us," Grandma answered.

"That makes no sense, Grandma."

"Just because you don't understand it, Annie, doesn't make it not so."

I didn't understand Grandma's point. But that's no surprise. I didn't understand most of the stuff that was said or done at church anyway. Stand up, sit down, shake hands, stand up, kneel, and sit down again. The stories the men read from the Bible did not make any sense, and when Father Weingartz delivered his homily, I thought for sure I would die from boredom.

"I imagine I will be assisting the Ladies Guild in preparing the luncheon for Mr. Dierick's funeral Mass."

"Can I help you bake the pies, Grandma?"

"Certainly, dear. Shall we make a few chocolate?"

"Sure! Can we make an extra one that I can take home?"

"You betcha," Grandma smiled.

We baked six pies. Grandma took five to the funeral luncheon, and I took a chocolate pie home.

The senseless killing of Mr. Diericks was just pure evil as far as I was concerned too. His attacker was never caught. I couldn't shake the feeling that maybe the bulldozers had unearthed the spirits of the Yam-Ko-Desh on the shores of Deer Lake. And it wasn't long before tragedy struck again. Michael Claus, a Clarkston High School senior, drown in Whipple Lake. Michael apparently fell out of his boat.[10] He was a good swimmer, and Whipple Lake isn't that big, so his death just didn't make any sense. Michael was an extremely handsome boy, the kind of boy any young girl would be smitten with. Not only was I deeply saddened by Michael's accident, the uneasiness I felt when we first moved to Clarkston returned, now stronger than ever.

*I was sitting on a stool next to Grandpa in the ice shanty. The lines of our tip-up poles deep down in the dark water through a hole Grandpa had cut through the ice. He was smoking a pipe. The smell of tobacco filled the small space. I had a fish on my line. I reached down to grab my pole. I slipped and fell through the hole into the water. The water was freezing cold and my heavy winter clothes made it hard for me to swim. I flailed my arms and kicked my legs as hard as I could. All I could see above my head was ice. Where was the hole? I could feel my lungs start to burn. I needed air. I am going to drown. Oh God, I am going to drown!*

I awoke from the nightmare with a start to a typical Michigan gray day. My bedroom door was slightly cracked open. Smokey was curled up next to me in his usual spot, still asleep. I laid there for a few minutes. I could faintly hear my parents' voices as they talked downstairs.

"You ready for some breakfast, sweet boy?" I asked Smokey stroking the soft fur on the top of his head. "You are getting to be an old man. Look at the white hair on your chin." Smokey loved to have his chin and neck scratched, so I obliged. I pulled back the covers, hopped out of bed, and headed down stairs. Smokey ran ahead of me. Mom and Dad were chatting at the kitchen table having their morning coffee when Smokey and I arrived for breakfast. Dad had his face in the paper. Mom had her face in a magazine.

"Killing people is just plain wrong, even if they are sick," Dad said.

"Clancy, she was not sick! She had arthritis. You don't put your wife *down* because she has arthritis!"

"He couldn't have been in his right mind to put his poor wife in the car and suffocate her in the garage like that. Even if she was sick, he shouldn't have done it."

Reaching for a pecan roll, I decided to join the conversation. "Who killed his wife?"

"Robert Waters," Dad said not looking up from the newspaper.[11]

"Do you know him?"

"He used to be a high school principal and football coach."

"Another murder, Dad. Don't you think that's odd? I keep trying to convince Mom and Grandma that there is something wrong in this town, but they don't listen to me. I think Grandma's exact words last time I brought it up were that I 'might be a bit soft in the head'."

"Yes, Annie, so your mother tells me. I think you may have a case of a bit of too much imagination going on in that pretty head of yours."

"We are just having more than our share of troubles this year," Mom chimed in.

"That's an understatement, Mom. What about Mr. Landon? How do you explain that? Poor man gets run over right in front of his house. Probably just went out to get his mail then the next thing you know, bang, lights out."[12]

"Accidents happen, sweetheart," Dad said dismissively.

"You guys just don't care. You never listen. I know something is wrong in this town. Maybe you will finally care if something happens to me!" I dropped the pecan roll on my plate and stormed away from the table.

"Kids," I heard Dad mutter as I headed back upstairs.

Thankfully, what I hadn't known was that Robert Waters wasn't the first coach to die recently. Clarkston High School baseball coach Rodney Treais drown at Deer Lake in two feet of water while he was teaching swimming lessons.[17] The kids he was teaching thought he was just swimming, but the poor guy was actually dead.

Monday had been a particularly rough school day. I got slammed with a bunch of homework and was in no mood to do it. I was laying on my bed leafing through some teen magazines. There was a loud knock on my door.

"Come in."

Patrick opened the door, came into my room, and sat on the bed.

"What's up?"

"Something happened today. I want to tell you myself so you won't freak all out when you heard about it."

"What happened?"

"Some kid got hit by a car."

"Boy or girl?"

"Boy. Nobody we know."

"Is he okay?"

"No, he's not. He's dead. But it was just an accident, Annie. Don't go freaking out on Mom and Dad about it."[13]

I didn't respond. I turned my attention back to my magazine trying to file away in a folder what my brother had just told me.

The paper reported that Robert Kuechle, a junior, was standing just six feet from his friends waiting to cross a road when a car struck and killed him. The paper reported it was a hit-and-run accident. Strangely, only Robert was hit, not any of the other boys who were standing right near him. The entire high school body was in shock. The high school kids were mourning the loss of one of their classmates. My elementary school classmates and I would soon be mourning the loss of one of our own.

It was February and I was terribly sick with the flu. I missed an entire week of school. When I was finally well enough to return, Mom baked cupcakes for me to take to class as a belated birthday treat. I was so excited. It made me popular, for about a millisecond. I settled into my desk chair, opened the desktop lid and took notice to all of the worksheets I'd missed and would have to take home. *Terrific.* I said to myself. I looked around the room and re-familiarized myself. Tony's desk had moved right next to Mr. Lane's. I wonder what he did wrong this time to get moved back by the teacher's desk. I noticed Jamie's desk was empty. Perhaps she caught the flu too. Jamie Bell wasn't missing from school because she had the flu. Someone told me at recess that she'd died after being struck by a car walking home from a friend's house. Jamie was twelve years old, the same age as me.[14]

Struggling to hold back tears all day, I felt such a sense of relief when the school day was over. The last thing I needed was for the mean girls to see me cry. They would tease me for being a baby and the torment would last for months. Luckily, I found an empty seat on the school bus for the ride home. I was grateful to be out of school. Alone on the school bus, my mind began to process Jamie's death. The bus driver turned on the flashing lights and pulled over to the side of the road. It was my stop. I hopped out of my seat and touched each row of seats to steady myself as I made my way to the front of the bus. I struggled against the fierce February wind for the half-mile walk home, unsure if the tears coming from my eyes were from grief or the brutal, cold wind. I slammed the back door, kicked off my shoes, and went directly upstairs. I slammed my bedroom door shut and fell down on the bed. I was lying there, forearm over my eyes, when I heard Mom's gentle knock. I didn't respond. She knocked again and slowly opened the door.

"Rough day?"

"Why didn't you tell me about Jamie Bell, Mom?" I asked without taking my arm off my face.

"I am so sorry, Annie, I didn't realize she was a friend of yours," she responded softly.

"That's not the point, Mom. Why are so many bad things happening? Is it Clarkston? Is it the Yam-Ko-Desh spirits? Maybe they are angry because those people dug up the ground around Deer Lake? And why are so many kids dying? Did they do something against God, and now they're being punished?"

"That is ridiculous, sweetheart. God doesn't punish His children. He protects His children."

"Then why didn't God protect Jamie, Mom?"

"You have to have faith, Annie. Faith that God is working all things out according to His plan for us, not ours. Whatever trials and tribulations we go through, it is according to God's plan."

"Now you sound like Grandma, Mom."

"Your grandmother is a wise woman. When your baby brother died, there was a period of time when I was very angry with God for taking him from me. Your grandmother helped me find peace. Those that God has taken were chosen, and they are in heaven. We don't cry for them, we cry for ourselves. We love our children, and to contemplate the loss of any child is perhaps the most painful possible human experience. Grandma reminded me that God knows this. Don't forget, He lost his only son."

Mom waited a few moments. When I didn't respond, she left me alone to sort it out.

I thought about everything she had just said. It was the first time I actually realized how much pain Mom must have felt when her baby died. Sadly, just a week later, Mr. and Mrs. Coventry would join in the pain my mom and Jamie's mom shared. Their son Mark was only eleven years old when he died in a tragic accident. Mark lived on Reese Road, the same road Patrick would almost die on come summertime. Mark and his two siblings were enjoying an afternoon of riding on a saucer behind a snowmobile when Mark flew out of the saucer and hit a tree.[15]

Scott Bell was just seven when he crashed his bike into the side of a moving car. Paper said he was riding down his driveway when his hand brake either didn't work, or he couldn't work it.[16]

# Twelve
# Tragedy Hits the Slopes

Clarkston had, and still has, a ski resort in town. Let me rephrase that. When I was young, Clarkston had a big ski hill with a few tow ropes and a couple of chair lifts. Today, Pine Knob Ski Resort has grown to seventeen runs. Not Aspen by any means but adequate for a few hours of good skiing when Mother Nature cooperates. The ski resort offers local kids a discount if they join the school's ski club. My friend Suzanne and I were ski club ski buddies. Mom would drop us off at the resort after school, and we would ski until closing time. If we had a good snowy Michigan winter, nothing was better than skiing.

It was a clear, crisp Friday evening. The kind of crisp winter evening that makes the snow crackle when you step on it and your nostrils stick together when you breathe in through your nose. I had been skiing the blue runs for over an hour. My fingers were cold, and I could hardly feel my toes. I had lost sight of Suzanne a few runs back. *She must have gone into the lodge to warm up.* Nearing the bottom of the run, I pressed my legs into a snowplow, slowing my decent down the hill. I passed under the chairlift and slowly came to a stop next to the ski racks. I pushed my goggles up on my head with my mittens and bent down to loosen my boot bindings. Commotion back near the chair lift caught my attention. The ski patrol was approaching the area I had passed just minutes before. *Someone must have taken a nasty fall.* I placed my skis in an empty slot in the ski rack and headed into the lodge.

Suzanne and some other classmates had scored seats at a table near a window with a great view of the ski hill. Window tables were hard to get on a Friday night. Helicopter parents usually scored those tables so they could stalk their kids. I dropped my gear on the table and headed to the counter for a cup of hot chocolate. When I returned, firefighters and EMS guys had joined the ski patrol under the chairlift.

"Someone must have taken a real nasty spill," I said as I sucked up the marshmallow foam from the top of the liquid in the Styrofoam cup.

"Looks real bad," Suzanne responded staring out the window at the scene that was unfolding.

Ten minutes or so passed and then news about the incident under the chairlift started to spread through the lodge. William Daeschner had fallen from the ski lift.[1] All of us ski club kids knew who William was because even though he only had one leg, he was an expert skier. The paper would later report there were no traces of drugs or alcohol in his system. No equipment malfunction could be found. And even with all the heavy Friday night ski traffic, there were no witnesses to his actual fall. It was a mystery as to how an expert skier just fell out of a chair lift to his death. Rumors circulated that it was a curse.

The remainder of winter passed without incident. The sweet smell of spring was in the air. I stopped half way to the car to breathe it in. Closing my eyes, I drew in a deep breath through my nose. The air smelled like God had put moist earth, grass, and spring blossoms into a scented candle and lit the flame. It was Easter Sunday. We arrived at church to find the altar decorated with exquisite Easter lilies. Father Weingartz was adorned with a festive purple vestment. Doreen and Danny and their family had arrived before us and were seated in their usual spot. It didn't take long before I was twitching in my seat. I would rather be anywhere than in church. My stomach was growling. All I had eaten for breakfast were a few bites of a milk chocolate bunny. I could hardly wait to get to Grandma's for ham and potato salad.

"And now for the church announcements," the alderman announced. I flounced in the pew and moaned.

"Oh, stop it, Annie. Mass will be over in just a few more minutes."

How in God's name Mom tolerated all this boredom for all the years she has been coming to church I will never know. I could hardly stand it. I had two speeds: fast and asleep. Mass made me want to sleep.

We went straight from St. Dan's to Walters Lake. Grandma and I were alone in the kitchen, so I decided to share with her the fact that I had just skied under the chairlift before William fell. The fact that William Daeschner fell out of the chair lift at Pine Knob just after I skied under it kept scratching at the back of my mind like a bad case of poison ivy.

"Do you think it could be possible that I am the curse, Grandma?"

"People don't get cursed, Annie. They get possessed. And you are hardly possessed."

Grandma put her arm around me and gave me a squeeze. She and I stood side by side silently peeling potatoes. I took notice of her hands. Grandma had tiny hands. The years of cooking and crocheting were visible. She had osteoarthritis. The bone spurs on her knuckles must have been painful, but she was a strong and prideful woman. She never complained.

Grandma was the first one to break the silence.

"Catholics have been battling against evil ever since Jesus instituted the Church upon Peter some two thousand years ago. You just keep praying to battle this town's evil, and we will win the fight. You'll see."

Well more folks needed to start praying. We were about to lose another battle in that war of evil.

Sadly, the spring of that year turned out to be just as deadly as the early winter. George Thomas died when the vehicle he was driving struck a parked car. George's car went airborne and landed in a tree. The nineteen-year-old was found alive at the scene but died before he arrived at the hospital. The newspaper reported that George was traveling on Maybee Road at a high rate of speed. He apparently did not even attempt to slow down before he plowed into another car. No one could understand or explain why George would do that. It just didn't make any sense. Nor did it make any sense nor was there an explanation as to why our neighbor, seventeen-year-old Deena Eller failed to stop her car at a well-marked intersection on Dixie Highway. Deena died when an oncoming vehicle struck her car.[2] It was as if both teens were in some kind of trance while they were behind the wheel. A deadly trance.

"Talk on the bus is that there really is a Clarkston Curse. It's not just me thinking it anymore, Mom. Other people think it now too," I announced stuffing a handful of Lay's potato chips into my mouth to fend off starvation until dinner.

"Nancy said that a curse is caused by a spirit and can cause misfortune to befall on a place."

"That's nonsense, Annie."

"It's not nonsense, Mom."

"There is no such thing as a Clarkston Curse. Curses are just superstition. Accidents happen. Accidents are just a fact of life. Now set the table for dinner, and stop listening to that nonsense on the bus."

I busied myself with setting the table while still thinking about The Curse. *I will have to find time to do some research on curses at the library.* I didn't care what my mom believed. A curse was the only explanation I had heard so far that made sense of all the tragedy that was happening in our small town.

I brought up the topic again at dinner that night. My conversation starter was asking my parents if they thought Mr. Bercheny had been possessed when he shot his wife in the woods in the back of their house.[3] My parents put a swift end to the conversation.

So, I tried a different approach as I cleared the dinner dishes from the table.

"I think we should ask Grandma if we can borrow one of her crucifixes, Mom. Did you know that the devil flees from Jesus on the cross?"

"Did you learn that in church? It would be a blessing to think that you are actually paying attention once in a while," Mom teased.

"I learned it from Doreen. She told me in Catechism. She said we should have a crucifix hanging on the wall like her Mom does and like Grandma does. It will keep the curse away from our house. So, since we don't have a crucifix hanging up on the wall, we need to get one. Oh yeah, and have it blessed by Father Weingartz. And place it in worthy place. Where do you think we should put it?"

"Anything else?" Mom smiled. "If it will make you feel better and get you to stop talking about this curse nonsense then ask your grandmother if she has a crucifix you can have. We will hang it up wherever you want."

"And get it blessed?" I asked.

"If you insist."

Grandma gave me a crucifix. It had been her mother's. It was made of walnut and was actually a secret box. The crucifix had two halves. The top half of the cross slid to reveal a hollow area in the bottom half. Great Grandma had nestled a small vial of holy water and two candles inside. Grandma took me to St. Daniel's to have it blessed. I still have that crucifix. Today it hangs in my own house.

Patrick and I often played with the Powe kids. The Powes owned a cattle farm on Reese Road, about a mile-long walk through the fields behind our property. The big, old farmhouse they lived in was over a hundred years old and in constant need of some sort of repair. The barbed wire fence that kept the cows in usually had a post or two down, which allowed the cows to escape. They'd eventually ended up in our garage. I surmised that the cows liked the shelter the three-car garage offered, three solid walls and a roof. Dad didn't think garage doors were a priority, so the garage doubled as a periodic shelter for cows. That was the kind of thinking by my father that usually started an argument between my parents, which ended with some reference by Mom that Dad was a hillbilly.

"Mom, the cows are back!" I hollered, slamming the door that led into the garage. I decided to exit our house through the sliding front porch door even though Dad didn't think having a front porch was a priority either. I would rather jump the four feet from the threshold to the dirt in the front yard than deal with the cows in the garage. There was one bull that was extremely mean and aggressive. If that damn bull spotted Patrick or me walking down the driveway, he would take chase. If cornered by a bull, Mom said it's best not to move too fast, but to back away from the bull slowly. Turning and running invites being chased, she said. Well trust me, that bull didn't need an incentive. Didn't matter how slow Patrick or I backed away, he took chase. And trust me when I tell you, it's pretty scary being chased by a mean, two-thousand-pound bull.

But that bull didn't scare Mom. She grabbed a broom and went out into the garage with Patrick. "Go!" Patsy distracted the bull with a broom so Patrick and I could make a dash down the driveway to catch the bus. It was quite a scene. Our mother in her bathrobe and curlers challenging a bull with a broom.

The bull dodging went on every few days until the snow flew. The cows would stop coming to our garage when the snow got deep, but they'd return in the spring. It didn't matter how many times Mom called Mr. Powe to complain, he just couldn't seem to keep the cows within the confines of their fence.

The next summer, Mr. Powe hired me and some other neighbor kids to help him fix fences so his cows wouldn't get out. He was paying each of us kids a quarter. I had to help Mom fix fences at home for free, so I thought getting paid a quarter was a fair deal. I took the hammer and one of the other girls took the can of nails, and we all took our quarters. I soon realized that fixing fence boards on our 40 acres was a lot different than fixing fence boards on the Powe's 278 acres. It wasn't too long before we all decided Mr. Powe needed the money more than we did. The other girls gave him his quarter back and left. I did not want to disappoint Mr. Powe, so I stuck it out the rest of the day, one fence board at a time. I never did it again.

"I thought you helped Mr. Powe repair his fence yesterday?" Mom asked me as she looked out the kitchen window.

"I did," I responded pouring milk into my cereal bowl.

"Then why do we have cows in our backyard? Jesus, Mary, and Joseph!"

She flung open the sliding door and started running across the yard. I looked out the window and watched in horror as Mom tried to chase the herd of cattle away from the sapling trees she had worked so hard to plant. But one incredibly angry Irish woman and several hundred sapling trees were no match for a herd of cattle. So, Mom did what any other irrational person would do under the circumstances. She marched into the barn, grabbed a lead line, and headed straight for the herd.

"What *is* she doing?" Patrick asked joining me at the window.

"I have no idea."

Mom appeared out of the middle of the herd with a small, white-faced Hereford calf. The calf had a lead line around his neck, and Mom was marching it straight to our barn.

"I guess we have ourselves a cow," Patrick laughed.

We watched her come through the fence turn style and head back toward the house. I could tell by her gate that she was furious. I met her at the back door.

"How bad is it?" I asked.

She slammed the door.

"They either ate or trampled every single one!"

I could tell by the look in her eyes she was ready to "spit nails" as Grandpa used to say. Mom picked up the telephone and started dialing.

My mom adored Mrs. Powe, but I could tell she was at the end of her rope with the entire cow situation.

"Barbara, it's Pat. Those damn cows of Dick's were over here again, and this time they destroyed hundreds of my saplings. You tell that husband of yours that I took one of his calves. It's in the barn, and I am selling it for damages. And be sure and tell him if he thinks of coming over here to try to take that calf back that I will shoot him on sight—No need to apologize, Barbara. It's not your fault. Just relay my message to Dick."

As angry as Mom was, she wouldn't be able to stay angry with Mr. Powe for long. He would save my brother's life just a few days later.

Patrick would often ride his dirt bike across the vacant land between our farm and the Powe's. Mom gave him one rule: Be home by dusk. One evening Patrick didn't come home, and it was quite a bit past dusk. It was actually quite dark outside. I could tell Mom was starting to worry. She kept looking out the kitchen window for any sign of my brother. Finally, she decided she better call over to the Powe's. Mr. Powe informed her that Patrick had left some time ago.

"Then he certainly should have arrived home by now, Dick. I will walk the bike trail to your place and see if I can find him. Perhaps he got a flat tire or something. I would appreciate it if you could do the same from your end."

Mom hung up the phone, told me to stay put, grabbed a flashlight, and rushed out of the house. She started hiking down the trail Patrick would have traveled home. Mr. Powe also grabbed a flashlight and started up the trail from the Reese Road side. Mr. Powe found Patrick and his dirt bike tangled up in an old barbed wire fence on the vacant land between our farms.

The kickstand of Patrick's dirt bike had impaled his calf upon impact with the fence. The kickstand tore the flesh of his leg from his calf up to his knee. My brother had lost an enormous amount of blood by the time he was found. Mr. Powe took off his shirt, made a tourniquet, and applied it to Patrick's leg. Mom arrived at the scene just as Mr. Powe was lifting him in his strong arms. With my mother leading the way with her flashlight, she and Mr. Powe trotted back to his farm. Mr. Powe drove Patrick and Mom to the hospital in his truck. Patrick was a very lucky boy that night. If not for Mr. Powe, Patrick would have bled to death in that field. So, Mom couldn't stay mad at Mr. Powe.

While waiting in the emergency room as Patrick underwent emergency surgery, Mr. Powe told Mom that he was thinking of selling the herd of cattle. There was a fella over on Pine Knob Road that was interested in buying the herd. He said the last time the cows had gotten out, they'd trampled over some neighbor's rabbit cages, and all their rabbits got out. The neighbor was so mad they'd called the sheriff.

Patrick came home from the hospital a week later with 127 staples in his leg. Mom spent the rest of the summer tending to him. My father spent the rest of the summer tending to his business and bottles of scotch. I spent the rest of the summer tending to the animals, cleaning stalls, and doing chores.

"Well I'll be damned. Dick made an entire spread in the paper," Dad chuckled.[4]

"Let me see!" I ran over and jumped on the arm of my dad's chair and began to read.

"I didn't know Mr. Powe's first name was Destry. What kind of a name is that!"

"What's the article say, Clancy?" Mom asked.

"Says here the complaints about Dick's cows getting loose got so bad he didn't know if the police were going to shoot him or the cows. Hey, Patsy, the article even mentions the calf you took hostage." Dad laughed. "Apparently, the police chief got as fed up as you. Says here the police have had to round the cows up six or seven times already this year, and last Sunday when they got out they couldn't even find them."

We all got a good chuckle out of the story. A week after Mr. Powe and his cattle made the paper, the cows were gone. Mom returned the calf to him so it could be sold with the rest of the herd. We eventually got garage doors. The Powe's old historic farmhouse and the grand old barn were bulldozed down to make room for more progress. A subdivision now sits where the grand old farm once stood.

The one thing I disliked almost as much as I disliked church was stacking hay in the barn. I was slight and not very strong. I couldn't avoid the hay rubbing on the skin of my arms as I struggled to pick up and stack the bales. By the time Mom would let me quit helping, my arms would be covered in an itchy rash.

"The Scramlin brothers are going to be dropping off two hundred and fifty bales of hay around eleven this morning. The hay has to be unloaded and stacked in the barn by two thirty this afternoon so they can pick up the trailer. Patrick, your father and I will take care of the hay if you run the manure spreader. I shoveled it full yesterday, and we're supposed to get storms later. If that manure gets wet we'll have a real mess."

"But I was going swimming at Leslie's house today, Mom," I complained. Leslie and her family built a house on Rattalee Lake Road, one with an in-ground heated swimming pool. It was the first time I'd ever seen an in-ground swimming pool. The water was so clear and warm. It was the coolest thing ever.

"Then you better get busy. I want the manure spread on the front five before you head over to Leslie's."

"But I don't know how to run the manure spreader, Mom," I said hoping the objection would get me out of the chore.

"You can drive the tractor, so you can run a manure spreader. Only difference is the PTO lever. It's a piece of cake. Your father is outside expecting you, so quick, finish breakfast and get dressed and get a move on."

There wasn't a cloud in the sky. Even though it was still morning, the temperature was already nearing eighty degrees. I thought it a good idea to work on my tan while I was riding around on the tractor. I put on my two-piece bathing suit, slathered my skin with baby oil, grabbed my sunglasses, and headed outside.

"Dad!" I yelled looking around the back yard.

"Over here," I heard from the back porch. Barefoot, I trotted up the wooden steps and announced I was ready to spread manure.

"Is that what you plan on wearing?" Dad asked me with a grin.

"Yep, I might as well get a tan while spreading horse crap," I said with an annoyed, pre-teen tone.

"Suit yourself. But put on some shoes."

With tennis shoes on my feet, I followed Dad to the pasture. He opened the gate's latch and swung it open. I marched past him and hopped up on the seat of the tractor. He handed me the keys.

"After you get out in the front five, just push in the clutch and push up this PTO lever, nice and slow. That's it."

After he was sure I understood his instructions, he told me to go ahead and fire up the tractor's engine. I started up the big machine, pushed in the clutch with my right food, put the tractor in gear, and headed for the front five-acre pasture. The first ten minutes or so went fine. And then I turned the corner. The wind was coming out of the north, picking up just as I turned the corner. The wind lifted up the light, dry horse manure and sent it flying in my direction. Within seconds, my baby-oiled skin was covered in horse shit. Dad was standing on the other side of the pasture fence laughing himself silly. I was not amused.

With the job of spreading the manure finally completed, I headed to the house to take a shower. The voices of my parents arguing met me at the back door. Patrick had been cranking on Dad for months to buy him another dirt bike. I stopped my approach and listened.

"I don't want you buying another motorcycle for our son," Mom argued. *That would not be a good idea,* I thought. Patrick was reckless. He was careless *and* reckless, a bad combination. But my brother had a way of wearing our dad down. Sure enough, a few weeks later, Dad and Patrick came back from running Saturday errands with a shiny, yellow, bigger dirt bike. Mom was furious. She and Dad had already had several heated arguments on the subject. Mom knew Patrick was reckless, and she was adamant he not get be given another motorcycle. Dad wanted to give

Patrick another chance. I thought Mom had won the argument. Apparently, Mom did too. I swear my dad did the opposite of what my mom wanted just to prove he was in charge. The man of the house.

My brother was twelve when he had his second motorcycle accident. Patrick was riding his big, new, shiny dirt bike down Oakhill Road. He was travelling way too fast. The driver of the vehicle that struck him said he didn't see Patrick's bike coming around the bend on the gravel road. Maybe The Curse put a spell on folks that made us kids invisible. Tina Smith got hit by a car right after she got off the school bus. Driver said he didn't see her or the flashing bus lights.[5] Maybe the driver didn't see Patrick. My brother had a neighbor boy on the back of his bike at the time of the accident.

I was helping Mom prepare dinner when the sheriff's officer came to the door. I answered the knock. Mom joined me when I hollered that the police were at the door. The officer informed my mother that her son had been involved in an accident with a motor vehicle. He and another boy were being transported by ambulance to the hospital.

The parents of the neighbor boy were already waiting in the emergency room when Mom and I arrived. The boy's mother looked at Mom with tears in her eyes and said, "Your son is trouble. He's reckless and dangerous. Keep him away from my son." Mom apologized as best as she could. She knew the boy's mother was right.

Both boys were bumped up pretty bad, and Patrick came home with a broken arm. But otherwise they were both just fine. I never saw that boy at our house again. The police had Patrick's motorcycle towed to our garage. It wouldn't be long before my brother talked Dad into getting it fixed. Mom was furious to say the least.

The third time was not a charm for Patrick. He made the July fifth issue of the *Clarkston News*: "Two youth injured in bike collision" was the headline.[6] Patrick and some of his close friends had made a motocross track on the hills in front of our house, complete with jumps. The boys always rode on the track clockwise. That was the rule. Some older town boys heard about the track and came over late one afternoon to ride on it. According to Patrick's friends, one of the older boys came up a hill going the wrong direction just as my brother was cresting the top. The two hit head on. Patrick was launched head first into a tree.

I was hanging out listening to eight-track tapes in my bedroom when Patrick's third accident happened. I heard Mom on the telephone. At first, I thought she was laughing hysterically, and then I realized she was crying hysterically. I came out of my room and snuck down the stairway to listen. Mom was on the telephone with Grandma, crying, asking her to come and get me. I sat on the stairs processing what I'd overhead my mom say. It seemed like an eternity passed before I heard the sirens.

While the ambulance transported Patrick to St. Joseph's Mercy Hospital in Pontiac, I waited at home for Grandma to pick me up. I packed an overnight bag and fed the animals. Sadie refused to eat. Dogs have an amazing ability to sense when things aren't right. She was certainly my brother's dog.

After dinner, I settled into the comfort of the Walters Lake house. Sitting quietly on Grandpa's footstool while he brushed my hair, I said a silent prayer for Patrick. I loved having my hair brushed. Grandpa knew it was the only way to keep me still so he could watch his favorite program, *Lawrence Welk*. The telephone rang. Grandma jumped off the couch and ran into the kitchen to answer it. Her telephone conversation lasted for quite a while. The volume on the television was too loud for me to make out what she was saying. Just as the television program ended, Grandma came back into the living room, a glass of Port in her hand.

"How is he, Ruth?"

"He has a broken jaw and a very serious head injury. The doctors won't know much more until he regains consciousness. He's in a comma, and they don't know how long he may be that way."

My grandparents exchanged a look. They had a way of communicating with a look. I guess that's what being married for fifty years does. It allows two people to develop their own non-verbal language.

"Annie, you will be staying here with Grandpa and me for a while. Tomorrow we will go pick up some of your things. Your mother has asked that I contact Lynn and Mrs. Cook and ask them to help look after the horses and the cat. Sadie can come here with us. I wish I had better news."

Despite the fact that Patrick was wearing a helmet, test results showed there was severe damage to the frontal lobe of his brain. When Patrick did regain consciousness many weeks later, he had the mental capacity of a small child. The doctors couldn't (or wouldn't) provide a long-term prognosis.

They advised my parents that time would tell. Patrick's condition was extremely difficult on Mom. When he eventually was released from the hospital months later, he was like a toddler in a teenager's body. He didn't sleep well, he cried, and was very impulsive. He was unable to focus, and he was restless and agitated. The only thing that seemed to calm him was Sadie. Resources for families dealing with head and brain trauma were limited in the 1970s. Mom became completely absorbed in what seemed to me to be an endless schedule of hospital tests and doctor appointments. At least she had her horses for emotional support. And Dad had scotch for his.

# Thirteen
# Tragedy Strikes Again

It was just after dark, and I was stretched out on my bed reading a Nancy Drew novel when I heard the first siren. Smokey was pressed up tight against my left thigh sound asleep. The first siren was joined by a second, and then a third. I gently skootched out of bed so as not to disturb the cat.

"Come in," Mom said responding to my knock on her bedroom door.

I opened the heavy, dark wood door and stuck my head inside. She was stretched out on top of her bed reading the most recent James Herriot novel. I got my love of reading from my mom.

"Do you hear all those sirens?" I asked. "Can we go see what's going on?"

Mom looked at me, searching my face, trying to read it. My mother knew me well. She knew I would fret about the sirens if she didn't go with me to see what was going on.

"Alright," she sighed, dog-earring the page she was reading and closed the book.

"Thanks, Mom, I'll get the keys."

Mom and I drove with the car windows down, following the sound of the sirens. We headed north on Rattalee Lake Road. A policeman stopped our progress at the intersection of Maceday

Lake Road. The policeman shined his flashlight into the driver's side window. Mom rolled her window down to talk to the officer.

"Can I help you, ma'am?"

"Just a concerned neighbor, Officer."

"A bad car accident has closed the road, ma'am. You need to turn your vehicle around."

He was all business.

Uncle John was up north, so we had to wait until the paper came out on Thursday to find out what happened. The paper reported that Elaine Campbell was driving with her husband when their car overturned not far from where Michael Claus drowned.[1] The article didn't give any other details. *Probably because there is no explanation or details to report. It's The Curse.* Sadly, her husband would die in the hospital a week later as a result of his injuries. They had four children.[2]

Only a week later, fourteen-year-old Dean Adams joined Mr. Campbell in death.[3] Dean was riding his bike to school on a Friday morning when a car struck and killed him. Dean was a ninth grader at the junior high. His classmates lost a second two months later when Rose Marie Perigo got hit by a truck.[4] I remember that Dean was a member of the choir. I was also in the choir. I love music, all kinds of music, but my favorite is country.

Mom loved country music too. She often had a John Denver or Johnny Cash album spinning. Recently, she switched it up with classical music. She read somewhere that classical music helps stimulate brain development.

She was doing everything and anything she could to try to stimulate Patrick's brain activity. She was also doing everything she could to get Patrick back to school.

The Clarkston School Board of Education didn't want my

brother to return to school. They felt his head injury caused him to have "special needs." Mom had been to several meetings with the school principal. He was sympathetic to Patrick's condition, but at the end of the day, he supported the school board.

"Your son's frontal lobe is his emotional control center and home to his personality," the school-board-appointed doctor explained. "The damage to your son's brain will affect his problem-solving ability, his memory, and his judgment, not to mention his impulse control. I doubt your son will be able to keep up academically or socially with the other children."

Mom was doing her best to control her temper. "I understand the challenges he will face. I certainly don't expect him to graduate with honors. But he will graduate with a high school diploma. I can assure you of that. With my support at home and my teaching background, I don't see any reason why it is not possible," she argued.

"Mrs. Johns, I understand your frustration," the principal interjected. "Our concern is that studies show that children who suffer from frontal lobe damage have difficulty interpreting feedback from their environment. We're concerned that your son may have difficulty with rules."

"*Patrick*," Mom said, "will follow your school rules. I will make sure of that. I will be driving him to school next Monday. I expect you to make any adjustments to his academic schedule that you see necessary, with the understanding that I expect him to receive a high school diploma. You can voice any more of your concerns to our attorney. Here is his card." She slid an attorney's business card across the table and excused herself from the meeting. The following Monday, she drove Patrick and I to school.

The school adjusted Patrick's class schedule so he had many of the same classes I had, which allowed me to assist him with assignments. Mom dedicated most of her time to helping Patrick with his studies, especially memorization. The poor kid had to spend hours working with Mom using flashcards just to get a passing exam grade. Patrick, although now a year behind schedule, did graduate with a high school diploma. He was blessed to have our mother as his advocate.

"I think Patrick has a crush on Liz." I elbowed Nancy, tilting my head in the direction of our siblings on the school bus.

Nancy looked at them flirting with each other a few seats up. "I think the feeling is mutual."

The bus driver flipped the switch for the red flashing lights and slowed the bus to a stop. Patrick got off the bus, but I stayed on. I was getting off a few stops later with Nancy and her sister.

"Is your dad going to be home?" I asked Nancy expectantly as we walked up the driveway.

"He should be."

"Oh good! Maybe he will play something for me."

I loved Nancy's dad. He was Polish, an immigrant as I recall. He always had a smile on his face and a harmonica in his pocket, which I never tired of hearing him play.

"Please, don't encourage him," Nancy said.

"How can you not just sit there and listen to your dad play that great old music for hours?"

"Because I hear it every day." Nancy gave me a friendly punch in the arm.

The three of us burst in the back door.

"How was school today, girls?" Mr. Rekawek asked as we walked into the kitchen.

"Good," all three of us responded in unison. Liz opened the cupboard doors looking for a snack. Nancy and I sat down at the kitchen table and started pulling books and papers out of our backpacks.

"Lots of homework?"

"Not too much," Nancy replied.

"Play us a tune while we get started? Please?" I asked.

Nancy rolled her eyes at me. Mr. Rekawek smiled at me, his eyes sparkling. He pulled a harmonica out of his pocket and began playing a Polish folk song. Nancy gave me that *really?* look. I stuck my tongue out at her in response.

We finished our homework and went downstairs to play pool and listen to our then favorite album, *Fly Like an Eagle* by the Steve Miller Band. I think Nancy and I wore a groove in the album that year.

Because of Mr. Rekawek, I was bitten by the harmonica bug, and I never got rid of the itch. I talked about learning to play the instrument all my life. Aunt Janet bought me my own harmonica when I was fifty years old as a Christmas gift. She said I needed to stop talking about playing and get busy playing. I bought *Harmonica for Dummies* and tried to teach myself, so far with little success.

Nancy eventually settled down in Maine. She got married and had two boys. Her parents retired and moved to the Traverse City area. Nancy visited Clarkston a few summers back. During that visit, I shared with her that I was struggling to teach myself how to play the harmonica. I asked her if she thought her dad would give me lessons if I drove up to visit him. Nancy found the fact that I was still infatuated with the harmonica amusing.

Nancy had a procedure done on her heart when she returned to Maine. I called her while she was in the hospital to check on her. We made plans to visit her parents together the following summer. We would never make the trip. Nancy died the next morning. Nancy was buried on her fifty-second birthday. Medically speaking, Nancy died from a heart condition. But I believe she died from a broken heart. One of her boys had been killed in a car accident a few years earlier. Time never dulled Nancy's pain.

Spring of 1974 came early and with exceptional beauty. I was hopeful that perhaps The Curse had been broken. Mom opened the dining room sliding door walls allowing fresh air and the afternoon sun to shine in. Its rays revealed tiny bits of dust on the top of the walnut table as I set it for dinner.

"Hello," Dad hollered as he shut the back door.

"Hey, Dad."

Dad handed me a stack of mail. I dropped the stack on the kitchen counter. The paper that was folded on top of the mail popped open: "Two Maceday youths drown."[5] My heart sank. *This just can't be.* We had been having such an exceptional spring. Nothing bad had happened since Patrick's accident. And he had survived it. I was so hopeful that meant The Curse had been broken. Spring is a time full of transformations. Spring is a time to move forward. I was hopeful this spring would be the spring Clarkston would move forward, away from all the tragedy. I picked up the paper and read the article.

The article reported that a kindergartener from Pine Knob Elementary school drowned in Maceday Lake. Two boys had gone for a walk in the woods after school on Wednesday afternoon and never returned. Six-year-old James Osborne was found floating in a cove fifteen feet from shore. Divers found his eleven-year-old cousin's body the following day. The two boys were buried not far from my baby brother in Lake View Cemetery.

I felt an urgent need to talk to Sue. I grabbed the desk phone from the credenza in the hallway. Pulling the cord as far as it would go, I went into my parent's bedroom and shut the door. Sue was my best friend in junior high. She had long, thick, black hair; long legs; and amazing eyes. Sue was genuine and fun. The farthest thing from a mean girl you could imagine. I dialed her telephone number. I got a busy signal. I waited a few minutes then tried again. The line was still busy. I decided to busy myself with some homework. After about thirty minutes, I tried Sue's telephone number one last time. The phone rang. *Finally!*

"Plummer residence," Sue's mom answered.

"Hello, Mrs. Plummer. It's Ann Johns. Can I speak with Sue, please?"

"We are in the middle of having dinner, Ann. Sue will have to call you back later."

I thanked Mrs. Plumber and hung up the phone.

I fidgeted at the dining room table the rest of the evening trying to concentrate on my homework while I waited for Sue to call me back. She didn't return my phone call that evening. Our conversation would have to wait until the following school day. I slept fitfully that night. My peaceful slumber interrupted frequently with bad dreams.

"Why didn't you call me back?" I asked Sue as we dialed the combinations on our lockers before first hour.

"I had homework to do, and my dad wouldn't let me use the phone. What's got you so on edge?" asked Sue slamming her locker door shut.

"The Curse is back. Two young boys drown in Maceday Lake."

Sue just stared at me. She had no words. Sue, like me, had been so hopeful The Curse had somehow been broken and was behind us.

"We're going to be late for gym," I finally said as I slammed my locker door shut. I headed toward the front of the school to the girl's locker room leaving Sue stunned, standing there.

"Wait up!"

I hated gym class. My disdain for gym class was right up there with church and stacking hay bales in the barn. Could there possibly be anything worse than stripping down to your underwear in a locker room full of cruel, mean, and judgmental teenagers? When the curriculum was volleyball, the mean girls would spike the ball trying to hit other girls in the face. In volleyball, the mean girls only had a chance to hit you when rotation put them at the net. But with dodge ball, kids are used as targets. The girls who were the biggest and meanest were rewarded for hitting other kids in the face. I hated gym class. I hated dodge ball. And then there was gymnastics week. I was horrible at gymnastics. I could not, and still cannot, do a cartwheel. Gym was not my thing.

"Mom, can you write me a note so I don't have to dress for gym today?" I asked shoving my books into my backpack.

"You are going to fail that gym class and have to take it over if you don't participate you know," Mom replied pouring her morning coffee.

"I started my period and have cramps," I lied.

Luckily, Mom wasn't up for an argument that early in the morning.

Mom and I had a stare down for about twenty seconds. I won.

"Bring me some paper and a pen."

I rifled through the kitchen junk drawer and found a scratch pad and pen. I handed them to her. Mom gave me *the look* searching my face to see if I was lying about my cramps or not. Mom sighed and took the scratch pad and pen from my hand. She wrote a note, tore the note off the pad, and handed it to me. I grabbed it, kissed her on the cheek, and headed out the door to catch the bus.

If a student didn't dress for gym, they were required to sit in the bleachers and watch the other kids play whatever the sport *de jour* was. So, I sat in the bleachers and watched the mean girls hurl dodge balls at other girls. The cheerleaders were off to one side of the gym practicing their gymnastics, some of them on the trampoline. I glanced up at the big clock. *Thank God, only five more minutes.* I reached into my backpack and pulled out a history book. I made the decision to cut my next class and hide out in the gym. I needed to cram for a history exam. Most of the girls had already headed to the locker room. A few hung back to put away some gym equipment.

I was engrossed in my history book when a loud noise followed by commotion down on the gym floor caught my attention. I looked up. There was a girl lying on the floor. I couldn't really see what was going on, but it appeared as though one of the gym teachers was administering first aid. The girl was just lying there on the floor, eyes closed. I got spooked when I heard the sirens approaching, so I snuck out of the gym. The accident victim was Pam Bowman. She was a sophomore. Pam was helping fold up a trampoline when a spring-loaded brace flew out of its socket and hit her in the head. Pam suffered a severe head injury that sent her to intensive care.[6]

I put the memory of Pam Bowman's accident into a file folder and turned my focus back to the history exam. Mom was out in the barn fussing with the horses. Patrick was upstairs in his room. I was at the kitchen table absorbed in study when Dad came home.

"Where's your mother?" he asked dropping the mail and the paper on the kitchen counter and heading to the liquor cabinet to fix himself a drink.

"You really need to ask?" I responded without looking up.

"Do you know what she's fixing for dinner?"

"The farrier just left, so I would say she's fixing nothing. So, my money is on The Nick," I replied.

*The Nick* was short for The Nickelodeon Restaurant. When we moved to Clarkston there were just a handful of places to go out to eat. We frequented The Nick at least twice a week for either lunch or dinner while our house was being built. It was the kind of place you could go into wearing your muck boots and with the smell of horse manure on your clothes. The Nick wasn't technically a restaurant. It was actually a party store with a delicatessen. The owners had installed a few wooden tables so the local folks could sit down and eat a sandwich and drink a cold beer. A large, old, very boisterous parrot greeted patrons as they entered the small seating area through saloon doors. Though small in number, the wooden booths were very spacious, more like picnic tables. The floors were dirt. Red and white checkered curtains hung on two small windows. The owners made the best ham and cheese on an onion roll you ever stuck in your face.

Just as I predicted, Mom came in from the barn and announced we were going to the Nickelodeon for dinner. Patrick went along. I chose to stay home and keep studying with the promise from Mom that she would bring home my favorite sandwich. I was thankful for the quiet study time. About forty-five minutes after they left, I decided to come up for air.

My neck was getting stiff. I sat up in the old kitchen chair and rolled my head from side to side trying to get the kinks out. I closed my eyes and rubbed the back of my neck.

"I need something to drink," I announced aloud to myself.

I fetched a glass from the kitchen cabinet, filled it with ice, and opened the liquor cabinet to get some ginger ale. I glanced down and saw the paper under the stack of mail. I began to reach into the cabinet for the ginger ale. I hesitated then slowly reached for the paper instead: "Boy killed in gun mishap" was the headline.[7] I couldn't believe it. A little four-year-old boy was accidently killed by his cousin with a pellet rifle. *Just a baby.* The paper reported that the boy's uncle owned a pellet gun that he used to shoot starlings that got near his birdhouses. James Wiggins was the boy's name. I flipped the paper over and returned my focus to the task at hand. Ginger ale. Sipping on my drink, I turned my attention to an article on the back of the paper, an article about that year's Michigan State Fair. I put the story of little James Wiggins out of my mind and into a file folder.

"The paper says local farmers will bring over eight thousand animals to the fairgrounds this year. Livestock representing every domestic animal from sheep, fowl, beef, dairy cattle, swine, goats, rabbits, and even pigeons,"[8] I read as we drove from Clarkston into Detroit for the fair. "Paper also says there are hundreds of entries for contests in vegetables, crafts, canning, table setting, and flower arranging." *Now that sounds boring.*

"Hey, Mom! There's a horseshow this year too. Imagine that!" I laughed.

"The fair has a very interesting history." Mom's years of teaching came out as we drove south on Woodward Avenue toward the fair grounds.

"The fair has been expanded to encourage understanding between our rural farms and the urban industry segment of Detroit. The latest machinery, an underwater excavator is a must see for you kids. And the Hall of Fine Arts Display too."

Mom's suggestions sounded incredibly boring to me. Animals were the only thing I really wanted to see. I didn't care much for rides or midway games. Patrick liked the midway games. Mom and

Dad did a good job of dividing up our time, so we all got to enjoy the fair. We had such a good time that we went several times that year. The ending of the two-week state fair signaled the end of summer. School started, the leaves changed color, the days got shorter, and the nights got cooler. Halloween would soon be upon us.

It was just before Halloween when Clarkston resident Robert Valentine was hit by a car and then run over by a second as he was crossing Telegraph Road.[9] The paper reported that no one knew why he ran out into the road, he just did. Perhaps he was running away from something, just like Charles Priebe appeared to be doing when he backed in front of a school bus. Witnesses say Charles was looking back at something no one else could see. Perhaps Robert Valentine did the same thing. Maybe something *was* there, something that only Charles and Robert saw.

"My brother Chris and a bunch of his friends are going out for Devil's Night this year. Wanna come?" Sue asked me as we approached her second-hour classroom.

"Are you kidding me?" I asked. "With all this weird shit going on around here, I wouldn't even *think* about going out on Devil's Night," I said to the back of Sue's head as she ducked into her class. I headed two doors down to my second-hour classroom. Sue decided to go out with her brother and his friends that Devil's night. I chose to say home. Not wanting to take any chances, I stayed home on Halloween night that year as well.

And I'm glad I did. It would be Smokey's last night. He died the next day. We buried that sweet old cat in the backyard. I don't know who shed more tears, me or Mom.

# Fourteen
# The Clarkston Curse

Tragedy wasn't reserved for just those who lived in our village; it was striking visitors as well. Twenty-one-year-old William Perkins was from out of town and in the process of moving to Clarkston when he died. He was killed in a motorcycle accident.[1] *Poor guy should have stayed where he was. Never come to town. And maybe we shouldn't have either.*

I was in a sullen mood when I arrived at school. I had been having bad nightmares recently and wasn't sleeping well. It was a daily struggle to wake up in the morning. I was exhausted. I was struggling to catch the bus on time. Mom put my alarm clock in a Farberware saucepan in hopes the metal pan would make it louder and actually wake me up. Even that didn't help. Mom had to come upstairs and practically drag me out of bed to go to school. I missed the bus again that morning. Mom had to drive me to school. She was as mad as a wet hen. Not a good start to the day.

"I tried to get my mom to write me a note so I didn't have to dress for gym today, but she wouldn't go for it. She was really mad I missed the bus again," I said to Sue as I tied my gym shoes.

"Why do you hate gym class so much? It's not that bad."

"It sucks. We get up way too early, get dressed, get to school to get undressed and re-dressed for forty minutes and then get undressed from our gym clothes and get dressed again. It's stupid."

Not only was I perturbed I had to get dressed in gym clothes, I wasn't happy that we had to go outside for gym today either. It was cold and gray outside.

"Wow, are you in a shit mood girlfriend."

Sue and I finished dressing for gym and stuffed our school clothes into a locker.

"Let's go, ladies!" the gym teacher yelled before blowing that obnoxious whistle she wore on a string around her neck.

"Come on, Ann. Suck it up," Sue said gently pushing me forward as we walked out of the locker room.

Our gym class walked out of the school in single file and headed toward the parking lot. We turned right onto the sidewalk that hugged the school driveway. The brisk morning air hit my legs. I wrapped my arms around my tee shirt, rubbing my hands up and down my bare arms.

"This sucks," I mumbled.

The boys were ahead of the girls, testosterone leading the charge. Sue was just ahead of me. I was at the back of the pack. A bus was coming down the driveway. For some reason the sight of the bus caught my attention. I instinctively knew something was wrong. I just felt it. I can't explain how I felt it, I just did. I stopped walking and just watched the bus approach.

"Come on, Ann!" Sue shouted.

I ignored her and just kept watching the bus. The bus traversed the drive and struck two students, Randy Fox and Bob Bradley.[2] I stood there, frozen. Staring. The gym teacher ran to the two boys. Several students were running back toward the school to get help. I just stood there, staring, processing what my eyes had just seen. Finally, Sue grabbed my arm and yanked me away from the scene, back toward the school. "Come on, let's get out of here."

"I still cannot believe that Randy and Bob were hit by a bus," Sue said as we walked toward the cafeteria for lunch.

"The whole school is talking about it. My math teacher told the class that he heard both boys were going to be okay, thank God."

Sue and I joined our fellow students in the hot lunch line. I grabbed a tray and set it down on the counter rails. The line moved slowly. I inched my way forward looking through the cafeteria glass to the food underneath. I didn't have an appetite. I decided on fries. I would have loved to have a Coke with that, but milk would have to do.

"Somebody has to do something," I said to Sue as I reached for a carton of milk.

"I agree Ann, but who and what?" Sue asked. "Your parents don't believe it's a curse and mine don't either. Our teachers won't entertain the idea, so what can we do?"

I was about to suggest we contact the newspaper when the cafeteria lady asked me what I would like from the limited selection.

"Just some French fries please," I said to the nondescript lady with the hair net. Sue got the same. We proceeded into the noisy cafeteria. We found seats at a table with Nancy and Cathi. We sat down and didn't discuss The Curse.

Just a month after Randy and Bob's bus incident, there was another bus incident. Gloria Young was hit by a car right after she got off at her stop on Sashabaw Road.[3] She survived. That same week, poor Mrs. Christ, for some unknown reason, turned her car right in front of a milk truck. She was not as lucky as Gloria. Mrs. Christ did not survive.[4]

I was bound and determined I was going to figure out where our town's evil was coming from. I became obsessed. When not in school, I spent every spare minute in the Clarkston library researching curses and our village's history. But all my effort was fruitless. There simply was no evidence that could explain all of the tragedy that was plaguing our small village. There was no mysterious murder from the 1800s, no craziness that I could find, no explanation at all.

Two years had gone by without incident. The year was 1976, the year of the bicentennial. My interests turned from curse sleuthing to boy watching. The Curse was in a file folder in the back of my mind. Jimmy Carter was elected President. Nadia Comaneci won the first perfect score in Olympic gymnastics. Sadly, Clarkston's bicentennial year began with the death of sixteen-year-old Karen MacGregor.[5] Our two year streak without incident had ended.

Karen lived on Almond Lane. Karen's car had gone off the road. She died when her vehicle struck a tree. The month was January, so it was highly possible that the roads were icy. Karen simply could have lost control of her car. Maybe her death was what Mom said it was, a terrible accident. Local school kids, including myself, weren't buying the accident theory. Rumors were spreading like wild fire that the Clarkston Curse was back.

I opened the front door of the small white house, went inside, and shut the door behind me. "Grandma?" I hollered.

The aroma of fresh baked pies filled the air. Apple pie, one of my favorites. I turned right into Grandma's tiny kitchen. Four pies were cooling on the white tile counter.

"Grandma?" I hollered again.

"Well what a nice surprise," Grandma said entering the kitchen.

"Mom was going to Lake Orion to run some errands, so I asked her to drop me off to visit with you. Who died?" I asked.

"Just because I baked some pies doesn't necessarily mean someone died."

"Well, it isn't a holiday or someone's birthday. So who died?"

I looked deep into Grandma's eyes. After a few long moments, she responded, "Mr. Gregor."

"What happened?"

"I don't know the details, Annie. It doesn't really matter now does it? Mr. Gregor is home with The Lord."

I could tell Grandma was keeping something from me, but I didn't want to push her.

"I wish I could stay and visit, sweetheart, but I need to get these pies over to the church."

"Let me help you," I said, grabbing two of the pies.

Mr. Gregor died a horrible death, a death he didn't deserve. He was a sweet old man who lived alone with a cute little dog as his only companion. Mr. Gregor was the kind of guy who chatted with anyone he met. The paper reported that two seventeen-year-old local boys, Steve Johnson and his buddy, Tim, broke into Mr. Gregor's home and beat him up. Then they strangled the poor man to death with a telephone cord.[6] Apparently, the boys did what they did for just the eighty dollars Mr. Gregor had on him. There is no explanation, not even a curse, to explain that kind of evil.

I rode to St. Daniel's with Grandma and helped her drop off the pies. Grandma chit chatted with some of the office staff while I took the pies into the church kitchen. We stopped at Rudy's to pick up a few groceries on the way home. Hundreds of pigeons took flight as Grandma pulled into the parking lot. As usual, Doreen was working at the cash register and greeted us as we walked in. The wonderful smell of fresh baked bread hit my nostrils. I chatted with Doreen while Rudy helped Grandma pick out a nice roast. Doreen had been working at Rudy's since we were kids. I suspect Rudy knew what abuse she endured at home and gave her a job to help keep her out of the house.

"I can't believe those two boys killed Mr. Gregor." Doreen shook her head in disgust, organizing some jam jars on the counter.

"Me either, Doreen. Don't even know what to say."

Grandma put the roast and some carrots down on the counter.

"Anything else Mrs. Tisch?" Doreen asked.

"I think I am all set honey. Please put it on my tab."

Doreen jotted down what Grandma had purchased and bagged the two items. I grabbed the bag and we headed out of the store.

After returning home Grandma and I decided to sit down by the lake for a spell. We were both lost in our own thoughts. The branches of the big willow tree swayed gently in the wind. A lone speed boat drove past, the wake water hitting the seawall a few minutes later. The sound of the splashing waves was hypnotic.

"Do you believe the Clarkston Curse can follow people out of Clarkston?" I asked, tossing breadcrumbs to the fish. "Mom says I shouldn't pay any attention to the gossip at school, but I think there really is a curse on Clarkston, Grandma."

"That's nonsense, darling."

"Come on, Grandma, what are the odds that a girl from Clarkston is in a motel room in Kentucky, and then some random guy decides to break into *her* room, and this random guy beats and strangles her? And this random girl killed by some random guy in a random hotel just happens to be from Clarkston? That cannot be coincidence! It is our town's evil, Grandma."[7]

"I just feel so bad about that poor girl. She just waited on your grandfather and me at The Nick a few weeks back. It won't be the same going into that restaurant without her being there. She has been waiting on us for years."

"It's a curse, Grandma. I know it is. I have been doing research at the library every chance I get, trying to find an explanation for what is going on around here. I haven't uncovered any historic event that would explain why our town is cursed. I am truly baffled. I did read, according to the Vatican, curses *are* real, and some can kill you. However, if you stay in a state of sanctifying grace the curses probably won't have much effect on you. So maybe the Clarkston Curse is only affecting those who don't stay in grace with God. What do you think?"

"God will protect his children, Annie, even if they fall from his grace."

Although Grandma seemed so sure, I was not convinced.

"Are you going to the fair this year?" Grandma asked, changing the subject. She was the master of changing a subject.

"Wouldn't miss it Grandma. There is a rock concert this year."

"I don't understand what you kids like about that loud music. I can't understand a word they are singing."

"Why don't you join me and my friends?"

Grandma laughed.

The 4-H Fair turned out to be the best ever that year. The 1976 fair had the usual farm stuff. There were over 1,600 kids competing in everything from western riding competition to knitting.[8] The fair hosted dog obedience trials, a livestock sale with over 100 steers, carnival rides, game booths and even fireworks. But the best thing in 1976 was that a rock concert had been added to the venue. The concert was held in main arena and some of the best Michigan rock bands performed.[9] It was my first concert. The music was incredible. At least as I remember it.

Grandma and I revisited the topic of curses following people out of town a few months later when another incident occurred. A local Clarkston girl, Pam Goeringer, was nearly swept over a forty-foot waterfall in Glacier National Park.[10] She was rescued just in the nick of time the paper reported. I was convinced it was The Curse that made her slip. Grandma, of course, thought that was ridiculous.

"Annie, if you don't stop feeding Velvet those pie experiments of yours, she won't be able to fit out the back door."

The big black Labrador gobbled up the last of my mini pies. Grandma and I were spending the day together baking. I was trying to educate her on music. Elton John's *Goodbye Yellow Brick Road* album played in the background as we chatted.

"Avid hikers don't just lose their footing in shallow water, Grandma."

"The Goeringer girl just tripped, sweetheart. It could happen to any of us." She rationalized.

"I don't believe she just tripped, Grandma. Something pushed her."

"Your curse theory exhausts me girl. How about we get this mess cleaned up and turn on the television? I don't want to miss the opening ceremonies," Grandma said, quickly changing the subject.

The opening ceremonies of the 1976 Summer Olympic Games were held on Saturday, July 17 in Montreal, Canada. Boxing was our family's favorite event to watch that year. And we weren't disappointed. Five American boxers won gold medals, including Sugar Ray Leonard and Leon Spinks. The team was labeled the greatest Olympic boxing team the United States had ever had. As much as I enjoyed the Summer Olympics, nothing could beat the Winter Olympic Games.

Figure skating was by far my favorite of the Winter Games. My favorite skater that year was Dorothy Hamill. She made quite a fashion trend, inspiring the popular wedge haircut. As much as I loved her skating, I personally, was not a fan of the wedge haircut.

Michigan's winter of 1976 was extremely cold and lasted far too long. Teenagers in Clarkston had two places to go to kill the boredom, Howe's Lanes bowling alley and the local movie theatre. My friends and I spend a lot of time in both. Barbara Lunsford was gunned down in the parking lot of the bowling alley in 1977.[11] She was a waitress there, and a nice lady.

The Clarkston Theatre was small, family owned, and had just one screen. The theatre featured films a month or so after they were released at the more popular, larger theaters. *The Poseidon Adventure* was the current feature film, and Sue really wanted to see it. I wasn't as enthusiastic. Town gossip was the theatre was haunted, so I was trying to stay clear of it. Gossip was that several different people saw the ghost of a little girl sitting on the theatre stage. A boy who worked there said he sometimes heard scratching noises when he cleaned up at night. Not only am I not a fan of wedge haircuts, I am not a fan of ghosts. But Sue really wanted to see *The Poseidon Adventure.* So I did what any good friend would do. I sucked it up and told her I would go to the movie. We didn't have a ghost sighting that day. Even though I've never experienced a paranormal incident in all the years I attended the theatre, apparently many others have. In fact, the theatre, although long since closed, is now listed in the Shadowlands Haunted Places index.[12] Oddly, the theatre is only a stone's throw from another of our town's locations that is listed in the Shadowlands Haunted Places index. Employees at the corner CVS store say they see a ghost of a man leave the store and walk down the road past the Theatre to the athletic club and back. The index implies it is a man from the 1800's who was slaughtered nearby. I believe it was in the spring time when the man died.

April showers brought May tragedy. On May fifth, another high school senior lost her life. Brenda Robins was driving down Ortonville Road when another car swerved from its lane and hit her head on. The paper reported that the sheriff's deputy couldn't explain why the other car swerved from its lane, it just did. That very same day an eighteen-year-old boy from California was visiting when he lost control of his car on a turn on Clarkston Road. He died when his car struck a tree. Fortunately, eight-year-old Richard Warden and seventeen-year-old Mark Dennis both survived the injuries they received when they each were struck by cars riding their bikes in two unrelated accidents that same weekend.[13]

"Open your books to page 227," Mr. McGrath commanded the history class as I slid into my desk in the back of the classroom.

"Thank you for joining us this morning, Miss Johns," he addressed me sarcastically, peering at me over his metal-rimmed glasses that had slid down his large, lumpy nose.

I didn't look up as I opened my text book. I could feel the stare of my fellow students as I tried to melt into my desk chair. It was Monday morning after the tragic weekend, making the students, myself included, anxious. I got caught up in hallway conversations about The Curse and found myself late for class, again. The fifty-minute history class seemed to drag on for hours. The year of 1976 had been the longest school year of my life. I was so looking forward to summer vacation. June was right around the corner, which meant baseball season was right around the corner. And I loved baseball.

June is the height of baseball season in Michigan, and there was no place better to watch a professional ball game than Detroit's Tiger Stadium. Tiger Stadium was located in Corktown, at the corner of Michigan and Trumbull streets. The Great Irish Potato Famine of the 1800s resulted in extensive Irish migration to the United States, my ancestors included. My great grandparents, like so many of the Detroit immigrants, came from County Cork, Ireland. Any able-bodied Irishman man who could scrape together enough money needed for passage to America came to help build the Ernie Canal, my descendants included. The neighborhood where they settled came to be known as Corktown.[14]

The corner of Michigan and Trumbull was the site for Detroit's pro baseball games for over one hundred years. The first game was played there on April 28, 1896, and the last on September 27, 1999. Tiger Stadium opened in 1912, six days after the Titanic sank.[15] Tiger Stadium saw exactly 11,111 home runs. Detroit's Robert Fick hit a grand slam as the last hit in the last game played there.[16] Now that is divine intervention right there if you ask me. For many Detroiters, however, Tiger Stadium was known simply as The Corner.

More than eleven thousand home runs were creamed at The Corner. Babe Ruth and Mickey Mantle hit the longest homerun hits of their careers at that stadium. By far the best part of the stadium was its size. Tiger Stadium was small and intimate. Intimate may seem like a strange word to describe a baseball stadium, but that's what it was.

We Detroiters love our local school baseball teams just as much as we love our Detroit Tigers. From little league games to high school games, it doesn't matter, we love them all.


"Let's put our blanket down over here in the grass," Nancy said as we walked behind the fence at home plate. It was June sixth, a Sunday, and a gorgeous summer evening. I was excited to get away from the isolation of our farm and be in town with friends. There was nothing better than sitting out on a blanket on a warm

Michigan evening watching baseball with friends. The Clarkston varsity team was expected to have a great season. They had some really good players that year, including Steve Howe.

Nancy and I were on the side of the school building sneaking a cigarette when we heard the screaming. We peeked around the corner toward the baseball diamond. A car was rolling down the hill. Two men were chasing it. The car was heading right toward a little boy who was sitting on a blanket not far from where we had placed ours. We watched in horror as the car struck the little boy, dragging him underneath it. The car stopped when it hit the baseball diamond fence. A spectator ran to the closest house for help. The fire department and police arrived first, an ambulance a short time later.

The little boy Nancy and I witnessed being drug underneath the car that evening was Danny Souheaver.[17] The paper reported that Danny's little four-year-old sister was sitting in the car and she somehow managed to get the car out of park.[18] Oddly though, the keys were not in the car at the time. Danny Souheaver went by ambulance to the hospital and made a full recovery. The Clarkston Varsity baseball team went on to win the State Championship that year, led by pitcher Steve Howe.[19]

The Howe boys lived on Walter's Lake, just a few docks down from our grandparents. Jeff was in my grade. His brother, Chris, was in Patrick's. Steve was the oldest of the Howe boys. He had become something of a local celebrity due to his talent as a baseball pitcher.

Sue and I were enjoying summer vacation out on Walters Lake.

"Grandma, Sue and I are taking the sailboat out," I yelled as we ran out the porch door heading toward the lake.

"Don't forget the life jackets!" Grandma yelled back.

I grabbed two floatable cushions out of Grandpa's fishing boat and tossed them in the sailboat.

"Let's sail down and see if the Howe boys are outside," Sue suggested.

"Then we can spill the boat and see if they swim out to help us," I laughed.

We were always coming up with some master plan to try to meet up with boys. There was no sign of the Howe boys that day, so we didn't spill the boat. We sailed and swam and sunbathed. Sue and I were both tired and sunburned when we finally came back in the house.

The lazy days of June rolled into the lazy days of July. I was sleeping in later and later as summer wore on. I dragged myself out of bed and arrived in the kitchen just as Mom and Aunt Janet were heading out on a trail ride. I had plans to meet Sue, Nancy, and some other girls at Deer Lake beach. I grabbed a quick breakfast, technically lunch, before hopping on my bike and heading to town.

Tree branches swayed from a gentle breeze as I passed by, coasting down the second Allen Road hill. Beams of sunlight shined through their leaves, dancing on the dirt road. My bike and I startled a little squirrel on the roads edge, he scurried under a pile of sticks and leaves. It was mid-July, my legs strong from months of bicycling. It didn't take long for me to cover the three or so miles to town. Hopping off my bike, I leaned it against the beach fence. I untied the towel I had wrapped under my bike seat and headed toward the entrance gate. I showed my annual beach pass to the attending lifeguard then took off in search of my friends. I found the girls slathered with baby oil, sprawled out on several blankets with the latest copies of *Teen* and *Tiger Beat*.

"Oh my God, Ann, did you hear about what happened to Cindy Pidd?" Sue asked me as I approached.

"No. What happened?" My stomach sank. *Please God, not another tragedy.*

Cindy had a job working as a lifeguard at the beach. I just saw her a few days before. She had graduated last year and left town to go to college, but she came home to work for the summer. Even though she was older than us, she was always very nice to my friends and me. Cindy had long, shiny, straight hair. I thought she favored Peggy Lipton from one of my favorite television shows, *The Mod Squad.*

"Cindy was walking home from the beach yesterday and a boat came off a trailer and squashed her against the fence."[20]

"Is she okay?" I asked.

"No, she died at the hospital."

"We just can't believe it," Nancy chimed in.

I spread out my beach towel next to Nancy's. Sitting down, I pulled my t-shirt over my head. I gazed out over the water. My friends were discussing the awful tragedy. I got lost in my own thoughts. There were children splashing. Some boys were taking turns pushing each other off the floating dock. A boat pulling a skier sped past. All seemed is as it should be, except it wasn't.

I didn't stay at the beach long that afternoon. I took a long route back home. The extra miles providing some much needed solitude. I didn't tell my parents what I had heard about Cindy. I knew it was The Curse that got her, and I didn't want to hear Mom or Dad discredit what I knew to be true. *I will wait until Thursday when the local paper comes out and see what the sheriff's office has to say.*

Mom didn't mention Cindy's accident to me either. She must've known about it with Uncle John being a first responder on the fire department and all. Clarkston was too small of a town not to have a story like that spread like wildfire. The topic of The Curse had become a sore subject in our house. The days dragged until Thursday when the paper came. Luck was on my side. Mom had decided to run to Ortonville to get horse feed about the time the paper was delivered.

Dust kicking up on Allen Road around 2:00 pm was a good indication the mail truck had arrived. And that particular Thursday was no exception. I ran down the driveway and grabbed the paper out of the box. Walking back to the house, I found the article about Cindy right away. The headline read: "Freak accident kills girl." The article reported that Cindy was walking home from her job as a lifeguard when a boat and trailer, being hauled by a car, hit her. The sheriff's deputy reported that the trailer met all safety qualifications. The trailer had "freakishly" become unhitched as the car went across the small bridge right near the beach. Cindy was pinned between the trailer and the fence. I folded up the paper and put it back in the mailbox.

# Fifteen
# Oakland County Child Killer

The Oakland County Child Killer's first victim was Mark Stebbins.[1] The killer abducted Mark while he was riding his bike home from the American Legion Hall. After being sexually assaulted and strangled to death, the killer laid out the twelve-year-old's body on a snow bank. Mark's lifeless body was found fully clothed in the outfit he had been wearing when he was last seen. The story of Mark's murder was broadcast all over the television and newspapers. County parents were keeping an extra close eye on their children after Mark's abduction, but they really pulled in the reins when a second child was murdered. Children weren't allowed to play outside without an adult. Parents no longer told their children to "get outside and play and don't come home until the streetlights come on." No more walking home from school instead of taking the bus on days when the weather was nice. Our innocence, freedom, and trust were shattered.

Jill Robinson was the second victim of the Oakland County child killer. Like Mark, Jill was also twelve years old when she died. She ran away from her home in Royal Oak with only her backpack following an argument with her mother. The day was Wednesday, December 2nd, 1976. Just one day after Jill disappeared, police found her bicycle behind a hobby store. Her body was found the day after Christmas in a snow bank along the side of I-75 with a shotgun blast to the face. Like Mark, Jill's body was discovered fully clothed, still wearing her backpack.

An entire year had passed, and the FBI had no suspect for the two murders. My parents were just starting to relax and loosen the reins on our whereabouts when Kristine Mihelich was murdered.[2] Ten-year-old Kristine was the youngest of the Oakland County child killer's victims. She was abducted just a few blocks from our old house. Kristine had purchased a magazine at a convenience store and then went missing. Her body was discovered nineteen days later fully clothed in a snow bank.

Timothy King was the killer's fourth known victim. He was abducted in March. I remember that day so clearly. It was one of those unusually warm spring days. Timothy was eleven years old when he borrowed thirty cents from his older sister and left his home to buy candy. The store clerk who sold him the candy was the last person to see Timothy alive. The clerk saw him in the parking lot talking to a man. After he vanished, his father went on television and made an emotional appeal, begging the abductor to release his son unharmed. The *Detroit News* published a letter that Timothy's mother wrote.[3] Mrs. King wrote that she hoped Timothy could come home soon so she could serve him his favorite meal, Kentucky Fried Chicken. Two teenagers found his body. His clothes were washed and pressed. The autopsy showed that Timothy had eaten fried chicken before he was sexually assaulted and suffocated.

The brutal deaths of the four children triggered, at that time, the largest police investigation in our country's history. The police linked the murders of the four children to the Oakland County child killer. Both boys were sexually abused. All four of the bodies were laid out neatly. All but Jill were suffocated. It was the first time television and the news media were used to try to track down a killer. Southeast Michigan was in a state of frenzy. The *Detroit News* offered a $100,000 reward, quite a sum forty years ago, for information leading to the capture of the killer. Although there were several suspects, dozens of theories, and many books written about the murders, they are still unsolved to this day.[4, 5]

"Mom, I'm riding my bike to town to meet some friends!" I yelled as I slammed the back door and ran out of the house.

"Oh no you're not young lady!" She replied sternly, following me out to the garage.

"Why can't I go to town? I told the girls I would meet them at Depot Park."

"You can go to town, but you can't ride your bike alone. These back roads are not safe for any child."

"I am not a child mother. I am fourteen!" I shot back.

"The police haven't caught the Oakland County child killer, so you're not riding your bike alone anywhere. I need to run to Rudy's anyhow, so I'll give you a ride."

I could tell by her tone that there was no point in arguing with her. I put the kickstand down on my bike and got in the car. Flounced into the car is more accurate. We traveled the five-minute drive in silence.

"I'll pick you up right here at four o'clock. Don't be late. And don't talk to strangers."

"No one stranger than you, Mom," I sassed as I got out of the station wagon and slammed the door.

Mom was hypersensitive to the whereabouts of my brother, me, and all of our friends. Most folks that didn't live in the village city limits lived on farms that were scattered 30 acres or more apart, our farm included.

Allen Road is a splendid dirt road, the prettiest in town if you ask me. Branches of the grand old ash and oak trees form a canopy making the road seem almost as if a tunnel made by nature. Today driveways scatter the road, nature's tunnel no longer visible. The road was just as beautiful in the winter as it was in the summer. A tunnel made of white rather than green.   Patrick's school crush turned from Liz to Beth. Beth lived just a few miles north of us on Allen Road. She was a year older than me. She was very pretty, a petite girl with big dark eyes and long thick black hair. She often rode her horse or her bike to our house to see Patrick, or to town to meet friends.

That same day Mom wouldn't let me ride my bike to town, Beth rode hers.[6] She was cresting the first hill south of our driveway when she noticed a man in a green pickup. His truck was pulled over to the side of the road and he was just standing beside his truck. The man grabbed Beth from her bike as she rode past him. Beth dropped to the ground and started screaming as loud as she could. She kept screaming all the while he was attempting to pick her up and drag her into his truck. A neighbor who lived a few acres up just happened to be turning off the lawn mower when he heard Beth's screams. The neighbor, who has long since moved and whose name I cannot recall, ran down his driveway and out to the road. The would-be abductor saw the neighbor coming, dropped Beth, jumped in his truck, and drove away. I don't recall Beth ever riding her bike down to our house again that summer.

Summer vacation was coming to an end. And sadly, so were the lives of two more of Clarkston's young people. Joe Echlin was driving on I-75 when he drove across the highway straight into an abutment.[7] The paper reported that he didn't even attempt to stop his car from driving into the concrete structure. I overheard

Grandma's bridge club friend say she thought that something must have possessed Joe's body and mind to make him drive straight into a wall and kill himself like that. The kids at school who knew Joe said there was no way Joe would kill himself on purpose. They said it must have been The Curse that killed him.

One of Grandma's neighbors, whose granddaughter was visiting from Illinois, was killed by The Curse too. Just around dinner time while riding her bicycle, the little girl got run over by a car.[8] Grandma baked the neighbor a chocolate pie. She baked an extra one for me. She dropped off the pie off at our house with a note to me. She wrote, *Don't over think it.*

"Another piece of pie, Clancy?" We had just finished dinner and it was my night to clean the kitchen.

"No thanks, Patsy."

Mom took his plate and dropped it into the sink, adding it to the pile of dishes.

"Paper says that your school has a new assistant principal, Annie."

"Yes, we do, Dad."

"That's all you have to say about it?"

"Yep."

Being an assistant principal at a high school full of teenagers is no easy task. Turns out our new assistant principal, John Kirchgessner, did a damn fine job. Teachers liked him, parents liked him, and the students respected him. Sadly, Mr. Kirchgessner's life ended in 1986 when he crashed his small airplane at the Oakland County Airport.[9]

# Sixteen
# Fires Burn

Deciding to cut classes, Nancy and I snuck out a side door of the high school and walked to town. It was a nice walk. Not too far really. Just far enough to stretch your legs and get a dose of fresh air. It was a Friday, the end to an exceptionally long week. Actually, it had been another exceptionally long school year. Perhaps all school years are long when you are a high school kid and its springtime. There was only one month left until summer vacation.

Nancy and I had an easy friendship. She was the kind of friend you could hang with and not have to say much. We were both comfortable in each other's quiet company. I was getting ready to ask Nancy a question about an essay we had to write in history class when I noticed heavy black smoke coming from somewhere right downtown.

"Oh my God, look!" I shouted, pointing westward.

"Holy shit!" exclaimed Nancy.

We started to jog toward town. I turned the corner onto Main Street and stopped dead in my tracks, causing Nancy to almost run straight into the back of me. I couldn't believe my eyes. Morgan's service station was engulfed in flames. Thick black smoke billowed out the windows of the small white structure, darkening the sky. Bystanders were jumping in the cars parked in Morgan's parking lot, driving them away from the fire.

Ironically, Morgan's service station sat right next door to the village fire station. But even that wouldn't help to save the place. The burning tires created such thick, black smoke that the fire-fighters couldn't see to get close enough to put out the fire. We could hear cans of oil and gas exploding. I just stood there watching, speechless, saddened by the loss of one of our oldest and most familiar reference points.

"Come on," Nancy said, pulling on my arm, leading me toward Rudy's and away from the danger of the blaze.

It took two dozen firefighters from the village's fire station, as well as additional firefighters from the neighboring towns of Waterford and Ortonville to put out that fire.[1] Mr. Morgan had been pumping gas and fixing cars for the residents of Clarkston since 1932. Back in those days, Morgan's was the only place around to purchase gasoline or get your car repaired. We didn't have a Belle Tire, Costco, or Sam's Club. If you needed gas, tires, or an oil change, you went to Morgan's.

The same week Morgan's burned to the ground, Gerald Van Tine almost drowned.[2] The paper reported Mr. Van Tine was swimming when suddenly, and for no explained reason, "something" pulled him under the water. After I read the article about Mr. Van Tine's near drowning, I refused to go swimming. Dad said I was being overly dramatic and that I shouldn't believe everything I read in the paper. I made excuses to my friends, avoiding going to Deer Lake beach. I wouldn't get into the water when I visited my grandparents either. My recurring drowning nightmare was back and the medication wasn't helping.

Mom told me years later that Dad had run into Mr. Van Tine at the Boat Bar several weeks after his near drowning incident. Mr. Van Tine told Dad the paper reported the story exactly as it was. There was no seaweed, no deep-sea creature, and no explanation as to what pulled him under the water causing him to almost drown. Maybe Mr. Van Tine just had a few too many at the Boat Bar my dad said, explaining away the incident.

The 1970s were a tumultuous time, and in many ways, a continuation of the 1960s: an era of drugs, sex, and rock-and-roll. At a time when the communication technology consisted only of a telephone hard wired to a wall, CB radios were becoming extremely popular. Mom and Dad bought Patrick one for his seventeenth birthday. Avoiding lake activities, I would often hang around my brother's room listening in on his radio conversations with other CBers. I was fifteen years old when I tagged along with Patrick to a CBer party. I was in the kitchen of a derelict farmhouse playing Euchre when a strawberry-blonde boy walked through the front door. The boy greeted Patrick and Billy. I never had much of a fancy for blonds, but it didn't matter. There was something about him. I was instantly smitten.

The boy was from the neighboring town of Ortonville. His name was Steve. It took a few minutes for him to turn in the direction of the kitchen. Looking up from my hand of cards, our eyes made contact. He smiled shyly at me, and I smiled shyly back. I never believed in love at first sight, at least not until I laid eyes on that strawberry-blond boy from Ortonville. Steve wasn't strikingly handsome. He was actually a bit too much the outdoorsy type for my liking. His hair needed a decent haircut, and his nose was too wide. But there was something appealing about his shy, sweet demeanor and his crooked smile.

Steve and I spent much of the summer of 1978 hanging out around the Miller Thoroughbred Horse Farm where Steve worked. Part of Steve's job was to take care of the evening feeding and clean the ten or so stalls. I often tagged along and helped to expedite the process. When the stalls were finished, we would take a ride on the

Miller's big green tractor. I would sit on Steve's lap while we talked and watched the sunset. The sky would turn from blue to periwinkle to a vibrant orange as the sun began its descent behind the earth. We watched as bats took flight in the evening sky to feast on mosquitos and other flying insects. The sweet smell of lilacs filled the air. Steve wrapped his strong arms around me, allowing me to recline against his chest. I looked up at his rugged face and smiled. He slowly brought his soft lips to meet mine. The summer of 1978 was the best summer of my adolescence. Morgan's wasn't the only fire that burned that summer.

Billy got his own fire burning. His fire burned with a local girl named Linda. Steve and I frequently ran with Billy and Linda. She and I found it kind of fitting that her boyfriend's dad owned the local funeral home, and my boyfriend's dad owned the local taxidermy.

"Check this out," Steve said, opening the door to the basement stairway at his parent's house. He flipped on the light switch. The stairs, carpeted in a beige plush carpet, were quite steep. They stopped at a wood paneled wall. I couldn't see what was around the corner. Steve descended the stairway two stairs at a time. He turned on another light switch at the bottom of the stairway.

"Come on."

Steve motioned for us to follow. He took a left turn at the bottom of the stairs. Billy, Linda, and I came down the stairway, turned the corner, and stopped dead in our tracks.

"Wow!" Billy exclaimed, doing a complete three-sixty as he took it all in. I didn't say a word. I just stood there amazed. I knew Steve's father was a collector of rare birds, but I couldn't believe the sight before my eyes. It was as if we had been transported into a zoo. Steve's dad had converted their entire basement into an animal museum of sorts. Floor to ceiling glass showcases, each completely full of stuffed exotic birds and other animals covered every wall of the expansive basement. Flamingos, mountain lions, mountain goats, beavers, and more filled the large space. I have never seen such a collection of taxidermy animals before or since. It was amazing. Steve was amazing.

The weather had been extremely hot. Storms were expected to kick off soon. We had finished Steve's evening chores and were just about to leave when a tiny fur face poked out from behind the stack of hay bales. It was the cutest fur face I ever laid eyes on.

"Here kitty, kitty." I crouched down low.

She didn't take her green eyes off of me.

"Here kitty, kitty."

Her eyes were oval and outlined in black as if someone had put eyeliner on her. A tiny pink nose sat in the middle of her face. Orange fur set off her eyes, making it look as though she had actual eyebrows. Her head and ears were black.

She cautiously came over to me. I picked her up. Her little purr motor started humming like a finely tuned race car. Steve put a push broom away, turned off the barn lights, and walked over to us.

"She's a cutie. There is a whole litter running around here somewhere. Sure likes you. Want to take her home?"

"Seriously?"

"Sure. Mr. Miller is always barking there are too many damn cats around here. He won't even know she's gone."

I threw my arms around Steve, almost squishing the kitten in the process.

"Wow. If I knew how happy a kitten would make you, I would have given you one sooner. Let's get the two of you home before the storms hit."

—

I don't think Mom really believed our story when we told her we found a kitten on the side of Allen Road. I don't make a habit out of lying, but if Mom had known I'd taken her from the Miller Farm, she might have made me take it back. I thought it best to play to her animal-humane side. It only took a few days for Mom to fall in love with the little calico kitten just as I had. I took the kitten  to see Doctor Alderman and make an appointment to get her fixed. The veterinarian confirmed the kitten was a girl. I named her Matilda. We called her Tildy for short, and it stuck.

Steve and I were inseparable. We spent every minute we possibly could together. Steve and I had one of those high school sweetheart relationships that many thought would last a lifetime, including me. But life doesn't always turn out as we plan. Steve's parents were about to throw a big wrench in my plans. We were sitting in the open hayloft door on the second story of his parents' barn watching the bats catch bugs. I loved those evenings. Steve and I would sit for hours watching the bats, holding hands, and talking about the future.

"I have some bad news." Steve reached to brush the hair from my face that the wind had placed there. I looked into his warm brown eyes and saw concern. My eyes scanned his face trying to read it. I could tell something was wrong. My mind started to race. *His parents took his driving privileges away again? He got fired from his job at the Miller Farm? Is he breaking up with me? What?*

"What's wrong?" I tried to hide the panic in my voice.

Steve looked away. I could tell he was getting choked up. He was having difficulty choosing his words.

"Steve, what is it?"

I could tell by his demeanor it was something serious, and I was getting scared.

"We're moving."

"What do you mean 'we're moving'? Who is we?"

"I am. My family is," Steve said softly.

"Why? When?"

"Tuesday."

"Tuesday! What are you talking about? Your dad has his taxidermy business. Your mom has her job. Your house doesn't even have a for sale sign up. What do you mean Tuesday?"

My heart was racing; I was trying to keep myself from having a panic attack.

"My dad got in some legal trouble, and we have to leave town. We're moving to Colorado. We leave on Tuesday."

Tears started to stream down my face. Steve was biting his lower lip trying not to cry. I was in shock. He put his strong arms around me. He held on tight as I started to cry.

The legal trouble Steve's dad got himself into didn't only make the Clarkston paper, it made the county paper, the *Oakland Press*. A Detroit federal grand jury indicted Steve's dad for violating a trade embargo with Rhodesia.[3] He was charged with illegally importing wild birds and over one hundred bird skins. He got busted in an undercover investigation by agents from the United States Fish and Wildlife Service. Steve told me his dad had struck a plea deal to stay out of jail. Apparently, there were some other guys from the University of Michigan involved. As part of the plea and his testimony, Steve's dad had to leave the State of Michigan.

Steve and I spent every minute together that our parents allowed the last few days before he moved. We promised each other we would be together as soon as I graduated high school. We would figure it out. I was heartbroken. Steve and his family moved to Aguilar, Colorado. Both of our parents were furious with the cost of our long-distance telephone calls. We were soon limited to one call a week. The letters, which started out frequent, became fewer and further apart. Our long-distance relationship died a slow death. Our best friends, Linda and Billy, were heartbroken too. They did their best to cheer me up. But hanging out together just wasn't the same without Steve.

After my first love left town, I spent most of my free time at Walters Lake trying to heal my broken heart. Grandma appreciated my company. She too was healing from a broken heart. Grandpa had died suddenly from a heart attack a few months earlier. His death was the first time I had experienced the death of someone I truly loved. It is difficult to describe how a broken heart feels. With Grandpa's death, I discovered that a broken heart isn't just an emotional pain but a physical pain as well. It makes your chest hurt, your stomach hurt, and even your head hurt.

Losing Steve so soon after losing Grandpa was just plain awful. Even though I didn't lose Steve through death, the pain was just as raw. I didn't realize a human body can produce so many tears. And time wasn't dulling the pain either. Grandma's strength was amazing. My heart ached after only being in love for a short time. Even though my grandparents had been married for over fifty years, Grandma seemed to be coping with her pain much better than I was coping with mine.

"Does it ever stop hurting?" I asked, placing my oar in the lake, gently pushing the water beside the canoe. I slowly brought the oar back out of the water letting the lake water drain off it before placing it back into the lake. Grandma placed her oar in the water and paddled. She didn't answer my question right away. Finally, she looked up at me thoughtfully and answered.

"The pain never stops, it just lessens."

We paddled in silence around the lake. Each of us lost in our own thoughts. A little muskrat swam alongside us for a while. We glided past the Howe house. Several turtles jumped off of a rock and into the lake as we approached. There was just a breath of breeze. No boats were on the lake, just our canoe. It was extremely peaceful.

After our canoe ride, I helped Grandma prepare lunch. It was nearing the end of August. August is a "grab bag" month in Michigan. One of those months of the year when you don't know what kind of weather you're going to get. That year, we had nice weather. Some years were cold and rainy. Grandma had invited Mrs. Rose over for chicken salad sandwiches and sun tea. While Grandma fussed over last minute lunch details, I decided to catch some sun.

I grabbed a beach towel, opened the back porch door, and let Velvet out ahead of me. The old black dog led the way, waddling down the hill to the water's edge. I spread the beach towel out over the soft green grass and settled down. Velvet found a nice shady spot under the large willow tree. The same spot we would bury her just a few short months later. It took Velvet a few turns around the grass to settle her old bones down. She was a grand old dog. I studied her large black head as she gazed out over the lake. The fur around her muzzle once black was now white. Where she once sat proudly watching every detail happening on the lake, she now closed her eyes and slept. Velvet had lived a long and happy life, and now she was tired. *Grandma is sure going to miss the old dog when she dies.*

The elderly ladies came down from the house joining Velvet and me. They sat under the shade of the picnic table umbrella. I was settled on my beach towel, eyes closed, letting the warm summer sun soak into my skin. I was just starting to doze off when something said in the ladies' conversation piqued my interested, bringing me back from the edge of sleep.

"What in the world was Leola thinking to walk out in front of a car like that?" Grandma asked.

"The paper said she darted out in front of the car, Ruth. That's a whole lot different than walking out in front of a car. If she was walking, the driver would have seen her coming and stopped," Mrs. Rose pointed out.[4]

"Mrs. Stageman's mind was possessed by The Curse," I chimed in from behind closed eyes.

"Did you hear what happened to Mr. Van Tine?" I asked. When I didn't hear any response, I continued.

"I'll tell you what happened. Mr. Van Tine was swimming and The Curse tried to pull him under the water and drown him."

"Annie is convinced we are cursed."

"We are Grandma! Oh my God, why won't you believe me?" I shot up on my beach towel and took off my sunglasses. I looked directly at Mrs. Rose.

"Just a few months back Billy Mosher was hit by a car, Morgan's gas station burns to the ground, and then there was that guy who was killed on his motorcycle. Oh yeah! And what about that boy from Canada who died? If he'd known there was a curse over Clarkston, he never would've visited here, and he'd still be alive! Same as that little girl from Lake Orion that was visiting friends when she was killed by a car!"[5, 6, 7]

"I didn't hear about the boy from Canada. What happened to him?" Mrs. Rose asked.

"There was a boy visiting here from Windsor. He got hit by a car walking down Sashabaw Road." "The poor dear. What a terrible accident." Grandma shook her head.

"Terrible accident? It wasn't a terrible accident. It was the Clarkston Curse! This poor foreign teenage kid was just walking down the road and the curse pushed him in front of a car. The car stops, the guy goes to get help, and then a second car comes by and runs over the kid again!"

"That is just awful!" Mrs. Rose exclaimed.

Grandma shot her a look. The *you-better-not-say-another-word* look.

Mrs. Rose kept her mouth shut.

"Whatever," I said rolling my eyes and laying back down on my beach towel. Mrs. Rose knew how much my curse theory drove Grandma nuts.

"I hear Rudy got some really nice whitefish in this morning." She was wise to change the subject.

# Seventeen
# Home Town Heroes

Rudy's Market was owned and operated by Rudy Schwarze. Rudy, a young butcher from Essen, Germany, opened his market in the 1930s. Rudy's Market was a reference point for those who grew up in town. Kids who once bought penny candy now brought their grandkids to the market. Rudy would buy, kill, and butcher his own beef, pigs, and chickens. And there are people, my family included, who would have gone hungry were it not for credit extended by Rudy when times were tough.[1]

Rudy was the sweetest man in town if you asked me. He was short and round with a jolly face. I could say he was almost as round as he was tall, but that would be an exaggeration. I never saw him wearing anything but a butcher's white apron and cap. Many of our feathered friends would have starved in the harsh Michigan winters if it hadn't been for the kindness of Rudy. For just as long as Mr. Morgan ran the service station downtown, Rudy Schwarze ran our village market. For thirty years he took care not only of us local humans but also a flock of birds. Each day over one hundred and fifty pigeons would hang out on the rooftop around the market waiting for Rudy to open up the back door and throw bird seed into the parking lot. Breakfast, lunch, and dinner. Rain or shine. No matter the weather, Rudy fed the birds.[2] His pigeon feedings were a ritual in town. Rudy eventually sold the store. The new owners weren't amused by the birds. I heard they took whatever measures necessary to rid themselves of those pigeons. Progress I guess.

Today I find myself feeling a touch of melancholy when I turn into Rudy's parking lot. No longer does my car scare up a bunch of pigeons. Sadly, the missing pigeons aren't the only change. I am no longer greeted by name nor is there a sweet old man in his white apron coat and cap asking me how many fish my Grandpa's been catching or when Grandma is going to stop in for a soup bone. Time changes things when you're from a small town. Some call it progress. I call it just plain sad.

"I need to stop at Rudy's and order our Thanksgiving turkey. Do you want to drive home from there?" Mom asked.

"I don't want to drive, Mom, so please stop asking me," I snapped, realizing as soon as the words came out of my mouth that I didn't need to be so harsh.

"I just don't understand you, girl. Most kids can't wait to take the wheel when they get their driver's permit."

I didn't respond. I had finished driver's training and had gotten my driver's permit a few months before. The truth of the matter was, I was afraid to drive. I was afraid of having an accident. Or worse, perhaps some random car would swerve into my lane and hit me head on. I didn't want to discuss the matter with my mother. She and Grandma both thought I had a dash of crazy.

Mom chatted with Rudy and ordered our Thanksgiving Day bird. I chatted with Doreen about nothing really. Mom picked up a loaf of fresh bread and a couple of peaches. Doreen rang up Mom's purchases and bagged them in a brown paper bag.

I approached the car first, heading toward the passenger's door. Mom handed me the brown paper grocery sack and opened the car door for me. She opened her mouth to say something. *Here we go,* I thought. She hesitated for a moment, decided saying whatever it was she was going to say, and headed toward the driver's side of the car.

"*Farmer's Almanac* says it's going to be an exceptionally rough winter I hear." Mom fastened her seatbelt and put the station wagon into reverse.

Weather technology in 1978 was not as sophisticated as it is today. But even so, forecasters were able to predict one of the most severe winter storms ever to hit the Great Lakes region.[3] It was Tuesday night, January 28th when Patrick hollered from his bedroom, "Hey Ann!"

"What?" I responded with a holler of my own from atop my bed, not looking up from my math homework.

"There is chatter all over the CB radio that a Winter Storm Watch has just been posted."

"For tomorrow?" I asked.

"Tomorrow night...maybe Wednesday we will have a snow day!"

Patrick really disliked school. I can't say I blame him. Patrick's closed-head injury made it difficult for him to concentrate, even on the simplest of assignments. He also didn't like the fact Mom made him drive me to school as a condition to having a car to drive. Quite frankly, I was a bit surprised our parents let him have the privilege of driving a car at all. Patrick, reckless and careless before his motorcycle accident, was even more volatile after his closed head injury. Perhaps Mom just wasn't up for the fight that would ensue if she didn't let him drive.

Patrick was getting impatient waiting in line behind the buses in the school driveway. We were listening to WRIF on the radio. The disc jockey was reporting that the storm watch was upgraded to a heavy snow warning.

"Woohoo!" Patrick bounced up and down in the driver's seat of old station wagon. "Let's hope we get enough snow so they cancel school. We can go snowmobiling and break the saucer out!"

The snow started to fall on Wednesday, and we awoke Thursday morning to blizzard conditions. All land and air traffic was cancelled. Dad couldn't even think of attempting to get out of the driveway to go to work. And it goes without saying, school was cancelled. I've never seen such a storm in all of my life, then or since. It took all four of us, fighting against the elements, to reach the barn to tend to the horses. After trudging through the deep snow against fierce wind, gusts up to one hundred miles per hour, Dad and Patrick were finally able to shovel a tunnel through the drifts so Mom and I we could access the barn stalls. When the storm subsided, it had dumped over forty inches of snow on Clarkston. The winds were so strong and the snow so deep that homes were actually buried. The Governor of Michigan declared a state of emergency, deploying the National Guard to help stranded motorists. Twenty people died as a result of the storm of 1978. One of the deaths from exposure happened in a stranded automobile. Almost one hundred thousand drivers abandoned their cars on southeast Michigan highways. The headline of the Clarkston paper read "Disaster Averted in '78 Storm."[4]

Luckily, for its residents, Clarkston was a farming community with no shortage of trucks and snowmobiles to help those stranded on the roads. Emergency shelters were set up at the fire station and the junior high school. Sheriff's deputy reported that over one hundred motorists were stranded in our community and had to be transported to safety. Mom sent Patrick and me to

Rudy's on snowmobiles to pick up essential groceries for us and our neighbors. The *Farmer's Almanac* sure got it right that time.

Winter turned to spring, and spring to summer. June was a month of celebration for Clarkston baseball fans. Our own Steve Howe broke all baseball pitching records at the University of Michigan. Some say Steve was the best pitcher U of M ever had on the mound. After college, the Los Angeles Dodgers signed him.[5] Everyone in Clarkston couldn't have been more proud that Steve was picked in the draft's first round. In baseball statistics, earned run average (ERA) is the mean of earned runs given up by a pitcher per nine innings pitched. An ERA under 4.00 is considered good, and anything under 3.00 is excellent. At 22 years old, our hometown hero pitched to a 2.66 ERA, saved seventeen games, and won the Rookie of the Year Award. Steve was the pride and joy of Clarkston.[6]

Dad's love for the game of baseball was just as passionate in 1979 as it was in 1942. He boasted often about the fact that Steve lived on Walters Lake and was, thus, a neighbor of my grandparents.

"How about that Steve Howe?" Dad, the devoted baseball fan, would ask anyone he thought cared.

"His folks live on Walters Lake you know. Neighbors of my in-laws. Annie goes to school with his younger brother. He's a pitcher for the Dodgers you know."

The Dodgers beat the Yankees in the World Series in 1981, with Steve throwing 3.2 scoreless innings to clinch the title in game six.[7] Clarkston's lefty golden boy, at just twenty-four years of age, had three incredible big league seasons. Steve clinched a Rookie of the Year Award, an All-Star Game, and a World Series title.[8] But then things started to unravel for our boy.

The kids I grew up with partied too much, including Steve. Perhaps we were just trying to dull the pain of the all the tragedy and loss in our small town. Or perhaps we were victims of growing up in the era of drugs, sex, and rock-and-roll. Unfortunately, with Steve's fame came money. And with money came expensive drugs. Expensive drugs meant cocaine.

Steve entered rehab for cocaine addiction in 1982. The Dodgers suspended him indefinitely after he missed a team flight. But Steve's lucky charm would land him with the Minnesota Twins. Sadly, he would suffer a drug relapse, so the Twins cut him too. He cleaned up his act and signed with the Rangers in 1987. The Rangers cut him after he failed to show up for a mandatory team workout. Alcohol, not cocaine, was Steve's problem this time.

It wasn't long after the Ranger's cut him that Clarkston's Steve Howe was back in action, drafted by the Yankees. Less than two months after he signed his contract, Steve found himself in trouble again. Steve relapsed and got busted for cocaine possession. Lucky for Steve, his attorney struck a plea deal reducing the felony charge of cocaine possession to a misdemeanor.[9] But Steve just couldn't stay out of trouble. He got himself arrested again. This time at the JFK Airport for possession of a loaded firearm. While this new legal entanglement played out, Steve continued to pitch for the Yankees. Impressively, Steve gave up just six runs in his first twenty-two innings. Our hometown hero saved six games for the Yankees that spring.

Steve's baseball career ended with the strike of 1995. After pitching for many teams over the span of seventeen years, Steve retired from baseball at the age of thirty-seven.[10] Two years after retiring, he crashed his motorcycle and ended up in intensive care with a collapsed lung and a ruptured trachea. He had been driving drunk. Steve recovered from his injuries, and the drunk driving charges were dropped due to a technicality.

The motorcycle accident was a wakeup call for Steve. He got out of the lime light, married, and had a couple of kids. He got into the energy drink business. It appeared he had gotten his life on track.

Steve was driving from his energy drink business in Arizona to his home in California on April 28th, 2006 when he rolled his pickup truck. Steve did not survive the accident. Our hometown hero was dead.[11]

# Eighteen

# Innocence Shattered

The spring of my high school junior year kicked off with a fiery head-on collision. For some unknown reason a car was going the wrong direction and struck an oncoming vehicle. A twenty-one-year-old boy and his friend died, burned beyond recognition.[1] Then just before Thanksgiving, three teenagers lost their lives on Seymour Lake Road when their Volkswagen collided with another vehicle.[3]

I took the stairs two at a time. I grabbed a towel out of the cabinet and turned on the shower. I had plans to meet up with friends in Depot Park, for a party of sorts. Not finding anything suitable to wear in my closet, I headed downstairs to check the clean laundry.

"I hear the deputies are taking steps to curb loitering in Depot Park, Annie. The neighbors are really starting to complain about the noise. I suggest you and your friends find somewhere else to hang out before you get yourselves arrested."

I didn't make eye contact as I responded, digging through a laundry basket.

"Arrested for what, Mom? We aren't doing anything wrong. Just hanging out."

"Nothing good is going to come from a bunch of teenagers congregating and loitering in the town park, especially after dark."

Not responding, I grabbed my *Night Moves* Bob Seger concert tee shirt out of the laundry basket and headed back upstairs. Hindsight being twenty-twenty, my friends and I should've adhered to Mom's advice.

Depot Park is a small park located in Clarkston's city center. Back in the '70s it was just an acre or so of land with some trees and a small river. The neighbor's complaints about teenage kids hanging out the park didn't stop us from doing so. After dark, inevitably one of the neighbors would call the police. A patrol car would show up and the cops would kick us out. The police were nice enough about it. They knew we weren't there to cause any trouble. They didn't come down on us for drinking beer or smoking an occasional joint of marijuana either. Perhaps they understood that we were just trying to dull the pain.[2]

We would sit on the park picnic tables or the roofs of our cars, windows down, listening to WRIF 101, our favorite Detroit rock-and-roll station. We never littered or vandalized anything. We just chilled. WRIF was playing a lot of tracks produced by our local musicians the night Joe died. Bob Seger, Ted Nugent, and Mitch Ryder filled the balmy air.

Joe Fry was one of my dearest friends. He was funny, sweet, and kind. Joe had a big crush on Sue. She wasn't interested in being his girlfriend because Joe was one year behind us in school. In those days, it wasn't cool to go steady with a boy a year younger than you. For some reason, I remember it was a Thursday when Joe died. A Thursday in July.

There must have been eight or ten kids hanging out at Depot Park that night. The boys were playing Frisbee, the girls just talking. I turned my head into the warm breeze and brushed a few wisps of hair away from my face. My eyes scanned the park. I hopped off the picnic table and approached a group of boys.

"Where's Joe?" I asked, not to anyone in particular, as my eyes scanned the park.

"He walked home," Joe's buddy responded, toking on a joint.

"Why would he do that? It's a long walk."

He just shrugged his shoulders, slowly blowing rings from his lips.

First friend rule is you don't let your friends go walk off alone in the dark. After a bit of discussion, some of the guys decided to drive down White Lake Road to see if they could find him. The night was pitch black. The guys drove extremely slow, trying to spot Joe walking. They found him just lying there in the road. A car came up behind their vehicle. Joe's buddy pulled his car over to the shoulder, allowing the vehicle to pass. The vehicle swerved around Joe's buddy's car, running right over Joe. The driver of the vehicle didn't even stop.

Joe was a practical joker, so maybe he was joshing his friends by playing dead. That is the only explanation that makes any sense as to why Joe was laying in the road. The paper reported that the driver of the vehicle who ran Joe over told the sheriff's deputy that he didn't even see Joe lying there.[3] He said he felt a couple of bumps, but he didn't realize he had hit anyone. The sheriff's deputy and the fire department's medical team did everything they could to save Joe's life, but he died at the scene. Joe's parents buried him in Sashabaw Plains Cemetery. I never hung out at Depot Park again.

Joe's parents wrote a letter to the editor of the paper thanking all the people in the community who supported them during the tragedy.[4] That is how Clarkston was back then-a small town where everyone knew each other and helped one another. It took a village to raise a child.

Thirty-five years later, my youngest daughter asked me if I could give her a ride to town and drop her off at Depot Park so she could hang with her friends. She was fifteen years old. Joe was sixteen when he died. I had to turn my head so she wouldn't see the tears in my eyes as she got out of the car. Time does not heal all wounds; it just dulls the pain.

I put the car in drive and headed back toward Main Street. I needed to pick up a few things at Rudy's before heading home. I walked through the door and had a flashback. I swore I saw Doreen stocking shelves out of the corner of my left eye. Doreen started stocking shelves in Rudy's in 1976. But it was just a flashback. Doreen didn't work at the store any more. The new owners fired her shortly after the press showed up at the store one day. I imagine the new owners didn't like the fact that one of their workers had a sister that was an accused murderer.

# Nineteen
# Death at the Drive-In

"Grandma, do you believe bad things come in threes?"

"Nope. I think that's just an old wive's tale. I think bad things happen when they happen."

"I don't believe in wives' tales or coincidences, Grandma. Seriously though. Why is everything in threes? Have you ever thought about it? When I was little, it was the three little pigs, Goldilocks and the three bears, and the three stooges. At church we have the Father, Son, and Holy Ghost. Everyone has three names. We say one, two, three, let's go. What is up with the threes?" I asked rhetorically, not actually expecting Grandma to answer. And she didn't.

In my world, bad things come in threes. Just a few weeks after Joe's shocking death, Mr. Valentino died in a fiery plane crash.[1] Grandpa had been friends with most of the local pilots, Mr. Valentino included. Mr. Valentino hit some tall concrete pipes shortly after takeoff from the local airport. His airplane smashed into pieces when it hit the ground behind a shop on White Lake Road. Just a short time after Mr. Valentino's fateful crash, another plane crash would claim the lives of two more Clarkston men.[2]

Arthur Binard and Frederick Saltmarsh were enjoying a day of fishing on the Au Sable River near Mr. Binard's cabin. The small plane they were flying in hit some trees during takeoff and crashed to the ground upside down. Mr. Binard's funeral service was held at St. Daniels. Grandma volunteered in the kitchen at the church preparing food after most of the funerals. I told her she should find another volunteer job that wasn't so depressing. She said it wasn't depressing but rather therapeutic. I didn't understand how preparing food for a funeral could be therapeutic. Hanging out with friends was my therapy.

Sue and I were sitting in the tall grass in the field behind our house, smoking cigarettes. We were seated Indian style, facing each other, not saying much, both of us lost in our own thoughts. Grasshoppers and Cicadas were performing an amazing orchestra all around us: Nature's concert. I was lost in the beautiful sound.

"I just saw Monica at a party last Saturday night," Sue said bringing me back to reality.

"I heard those sick bastards cut her tits off, Ann," Sue looked up toward the sky blowing out her cigarette smoke.

I searched for words with which to respond but failed. Our town's evil punched me in the gut when Kyle Johnson bludgeoned his girlfriend to death in the woods off a local country road. Monica Hockey was twenty years old when Kyle bashed her head in and left her for dead. Kyle and his friend Jeff Coyle tried to hide her body under bags of garbage. Of all the death, tragedy, and evil I grew up with, Monica's murder hit me the hardest. Punched me in the gut is more like it. Maybe because she died at the hands of her boyfriend. Kyle should have loved and protected her.[3] But instead, he murdered her. I didn't know Monica well. We had spoken a few times at various parties around town. Monica was a few years older than me. She dropped out of school in eleventh grade to go work in a General Motors plant.

I remember Monica as being a bit of a chubby girl. She had big boobs, always wore a baseball hat, a ponytail pulled through the hole in the back. Sue knew her better. Sue had three older brothers, so she knew the older kids in town better than I did.

Sue was visibly shaken about Monica's death. In an attempt to get her mind off the subject of murder, I changed the subject to the upcoming weekend's social plans.

"Linda wants me to come over to Billy's and play cards with them and one of Billy's friends, but I am not so sure I want to go," I shared.

"Who's the friend?"

"Wayne Denny."

"He is a stoned fox, girl! You need to get over Steve, girlfriend. It's time. If you won't go voluntarily, I swear I will drag you there."

I wasn't so keen on the idea, but maybe Sue was right. Perhaps I just needed to get out there and date another guy. So I caved in and went over to Billy's the following Saturday night.


Wayne wasn't like Steve at all. Steve was fair, sweet, and shy. Wayne was dark, boisterous, and confident. Linda and Billy missed Steve almost as much as I did, including our late night Euchre card games. I can't say I liked Wayne all that well. I wasn't particularly attracted to him, but he seemed very interested in me. Wayne was a senior and very popular, used to getting what he wanted. I was a lamb being led to slaughter.

"Way to go girl, you went out with Wayne Saturday night?" Barb asked me as I was twirling the combination on my locker Monday morning.

"How do you know what I did Saturday night? We just played some cards, not a big deal."

"Not a big deal? He is a fox girl!" Barb laughed and punched me in the arm. That way-to-go kind of punch.

Barb's comment would be the first of many I received in school that week as rumors spread that I had been out with Wayne. Seniors I didn't even know, many of them Wayne's friends, were saying hello to me in school hallways between classes. Classmates, who prior to my "date" had no idea who I was, were all of the sudden making small talk with me. Linda encouraged our relationship. I think she liked having me dating a friend of Billy's. I admit it felt good to be playing cards on Saturday nights again. *Wayne is kind of cool,* I rationalized. *He's so popular. I'm lucky to have him interested in me.* I'm not really sure how the relationship transformed from Saturday night cards to me totally losing myself and being controlled by this boy, but it did. And it lasted until I graduated from high school. It wasn't a pattern I learned at home. Dad was a drunk but not a physical abuser. And no man controlled my mom. I think perhaps it was the role I played in our family. I learned to be a pleaser, a peacemaker, and an enabler.

Wayne would wait for me in the parking lot before school. He drove a small pale yellow compact car. I think it was a Chevy Chevette, not that it matters any. Wayne insisted he drive me to school. I didn't want to drive to school with him. So, I lied. I told him my dad wouldn't allow it. Since Wayne couldn't drive me to school, he would sometimes park his crappy little yellow car in the school parking lot, lean against it, arms crossed, and wait for me to get off the bus. On nice days, I preferred to ride my bike. If I got up and going early enough I would stop at Rudy's on the way and get a Coke to stash in my backpack for lunch hour. If Rudy saw me in the store, he would insist I take a donut, free of charge.

"Hey, Ann," I heard a familiar voice as I leaned my bike up against the front of Rudy's building. I turned toward the voice.

"Hi Jack, what's up?"

Jack hopped off his bike and leaned it up against mine. Jack Thompson was a good friend of Patrick's. Jack was getting a pop and a donut too. We walked out of Rudy's together. We ate our donuts leaning up against the brick storefront, making meaningless small talk. Then we hopped on our bikes and rode the few blocks to school together. That's how my friends and I rolled. We were boys and girls. We were all friends not lovers. Most families in town had more than a few children, so siblings were friends with their siblings' friends. There were a few kids who had hooked up and were couples, but for the most part, we were all just friends. Patrick and Jack would coincidentally share a jail cell many years later. Sadly, Jack died much too young, in his late thirties, I believe, from too many years of hard living combined with being in the wrong place at the wrong time.

I didn't notice Wayne leaning against his car that morning as I coasted up to the bike rack. I was unwinding the rope bike lock from my seat when I heard his voice.

"What were you doing with Jack?"

Wayne stood there glaring at me. He was breathing through his nose. His nostrils were flaring. His eyes were dark, freakishly dark. His hands were down at his sides, and he was opening and closing his fists. Clenching them really. Open and shut, open and shut.

"I ran into him at Rudy's, and we rode to school together. What's the big deal?"

I could tell by Wayne's body language he was angry. But for what I had no idea. I was turning my attention back toward locking up my bike when I felt the blow. At first, I didn't comprehend what had happened. I reached up toward my mouth and touched my lips. I pulled my hand away. Blood covered my fingertips. I looked around to see if anyone else saw what had just happened. Wayne's hands were back at his sides. He continued to glare at me.

"Don't ever ride your bike to school again. Take the bus."

That was all Wayne had to say after belting me in the face. He turned and walked into the school. He left me standing there, tears starting to well up in my eyes. I picked up my backpack and ran toward the front entrance.

The five-minute warning bell was ringing. Last minute students were rushing toward the front doors, oblivious to me or my predicament. I headed straight for the girls' bathroom. I cleaned my face up as best I could. I was going to be late for first hour. *Shit.*

My first-hour course that semester was Business Machines. I can't recall the teacher's name, but she was short and round with extremely short salt and pepper hair. School policy dictated that she ask me for a hall pass. She didn't ask me for a pass as I passed her desk. Mrs. Short and Round probably took one look at me and knew I was a hot mess. She let me slide into my seat without question. I tried to hide my face by looking out the window until my fellow students stopped staring at the late arrival. Sue sat right next to me in first hour.

"Look at me!" she demanded in a hushed voice. I turned and as strongly as I could muster responded, "What?"

"What the fuck happened to your face?"

"I fell off my bike."

"*Really*?" Sue asked sarcastically.

"Really."

Sue didn't say anything else. She stared into my eyes trying to detect if I was lying. I lied. I was scared of Wayne, and I was embarrassed. I didn't know what to do. No man had ever hit me before. Ever. Not even a spanking from my dad.

When I got home from school that day, Mom asked me what had happened to my face. I told her that I'd gotten hit in the face with the bathroom door at school. I made up a cockamamie story about some girl rushing out of the bathroom just as I was going in. I don't really know why I lied. Why does any abused woman lie? I think it's the shame and embarrassment. And I felt Mom had her hands full dealing with Patrick's behavior issues, Dad's drinking, and the constant financial pressures his business brought. I didn't want to be any trouble. I was anxious and worried that she would question my story or probe me for more information, but she didn't. I immersed myself in my school work, figuring my fat lip would heal in a few days. Wayne was just having a bad day, I was sure it wouldn't happen again. I put the incident into a file folder and shut the drawer. Tomorrow would be a new day.

My inhales drew in the cool, crisp morning air, my breath visible as I exhaled. It was barely daybreak as I headed to the bus stop. A light fog hung in the air, just above the pasture grass. It was so quiet, the sound of the interstate traffic several miles away was just barely audible. I kept my hands warm, deep in the pockets of my jean jacket as I walked up the hill. I arrived at my designated stop just as the big yellow bus approached, lights flashing. The bus stopped, the doors opened, and I swiftly hopped up its few steps.

Nancy was sitting in her usual spot, five rows back on the left. I plopped in the seat next to her. I reached for the book, *Go Ask Alice*, on Nancy's lap.

"Any good?" I asked.

"It's okay, a bit depressing."

"What's it about?"

"The life of some girl who becomes a drug addict. Speaking of drugs, I hear Tom has some good size doobies. He'll be selling them in the smoking area outside at first lunch today. Just in case you know of anyone who's interested."

The high school had a designated outdoor smoking area for kids who were eighteen years old. A lot of the seniors turned eighteen before they graduated. That smoking area was a hot bed for dope sales. Mostly pot, hash, and acid, occasionally LSD and PCP. The school drug problem was growing. The police assembled a special task force to try to deal with the issue. The Oakland County Narcotics Enforcement Team (NET) reported that the majority of the offenders were between the ages of sixteen and twenty-five. The county didn't need a task force to gather that statistic. All NET had to do was interview a few high school kids. In our small county, there were over 307 arrests and over four million dollars' worth of illegal drugs seized that year. Clarkston clearly had a problem, and Patrick had become one of the local buyers and sellers.[7]

Doctors had prescribed Patrick various medications hoping they would help treat his neurological problems. He often sold or traded them for street drugs at school. By the late 1980s, Patrick's addiction turned from prescription medications and marijuana to crack cocaine.

Cocaine combined with a closed head injury is the perfect recipe for disaster. Patrick suffered from severe depression and paranoia, which led to irritability and mood disturbances. Patrick would switch from extreme highs to extreme lows in a matter of minutes.

He would borrow money from Dad, steal money from Mom's purse, and steal things from around the house to fund his addiction. He would occasionally take one of our parents' cars into the drug-infested neighborhoods of Pontiac and be gone for days.

Patrick, like most addicts, isn't a bad person. He did what all addicts do best, manipulate. Manipulation is an addict's best friend. After having gone missing for a couple of days, Patrick, strung out and in debt to a drug dealer, would call Dad. My brother would beg and cry and tell Dad that the drug dealer wouldn't let him leave because Patrick owed him money. Our dad would go into dangerous, drug-infested neighborhoods, driving around until he saw the family car. Dad would pay off Patrick's debt. Patrick would swear on his life he would never do this sort of thing again. Dad would swear he was never going to bail him out again. But of course, they both did it again and again. This melodrama of drug abuse by my brother and enabling by my father continued until the day my Dad died.

Dad quit drinking in 1979. He went from being a hard-core alcoholic to a first-class enabler. He would cover up for, protect, and make excuses for Patrick's bad behavior. Patrick has been busted many times for drug possession. In July of 1992, he got arrested for robbery and reckless driving while attempting to steal a lady's purse in the K-Mart parking lot. Dad posted the six-thousand-dollar bond ordered by the judge to get Patrick out of jail. Patrick agreed to a plea deal that got him one year in the county jail and three years of probation along with alcohol and drug abuse therapy. Our father hired another attorney who was able to get Patrick's case reassigned to another judge. In March of 1993, the lawyer filed a motion with the new judge claiming that Patrick's head injury clouded his good judgement. Patrick's sentence was reduced to home confinement and probation.

Perhaps I inherited my father's enabling tendencies, which is why I enabled Wayne. Rather than tell someone about the emotional and physical abuse I was enduring, I made excuses for it. Wayne didn't have just one bad day, he had many bad days. I would make up excuses for how I got the fat lips and the bruises. One of the pamphlets Dad brought home from an AA meeting said that you may be an enabler if you have a hard time expressing your feelings, if you keep all your emotions inside, if you minimize the situation, or think the problem will get better later. Addiction not only creates enablers, it creates codependents, and I was both. My behavior as a child started as a well-intentioned desire to help, but as I grew into a teenager facing adult situations, I found myself over-functioning and my family increasingly under-functioning. I was like a miniature adult. I read somewhere that survivors of dysfunctional families have an exaggerated sense of responsibility. They tend to overwork and forget to take care of themselves. Yep, that is me.

Mom spent most of her time with the horses. Dad was rarely, if ever, home. On the occasion he was home, he and Mom argued. Their arguments usually started as calm disagreements, but gradually they got louder and more intense.

*There they go again. Mom and Dad argued for just near an hour.* I heard the back door slam shut. The house got really quiet. *That's odd.* I went downstairs. Mom was sitting at the kitchen table, her head between her hands. She looked up as I approached the kitchen.

"Your father and I are getting a divorce," Mom announced.

I was a junior in high school. Dad left the farm on Allen Road and moved into an apartment. Our stay-at-home mother had to get a full-time job. Patrick was in and out of jail, so I picked up the slack around the farm. I lost myself in schoolwork and chores. I no longer had time to think about my curse theory.

I pulled the shower curtain back and stepped out of the bathtub. Taking a towel from the top of the stack that was piled on my bathroom counter, I smeared steam from the mirror. I studied my reflection as I brushed my long brown hair, parting it in the middle. I moved closer to the mirror to get a good look at the pimple I had noticed that morning. It hadn't gotten any bigger, so a little makeup would take care of it. I resembled my mother, except for my eyes. I inherited my father's green, slightly droopy, Scottish eyes. Dad's friend Willard called them bedroom eyes. My frame was slight, my breasts, hands, and feet small, like my grandmother. I had a small waist with fuller hips. I was reaching for the lotion when I heard Mom holler something. I opened the bathroom door. "Annie, telephone!" she yelled up the stairs.

Coming out of the bathroom, I took the stairs, two at a time, to answer the call. Holding my towel closed with my right hand, I picked up the console telephone with my left. I pulled the long phone cord into Mom's bedroom and shut the door.

"Hello?"

It was Linda on the other end. Linda, Billy, Wayne, and I had plans to go see a horror movie at the drive-in theatre with a group of friends later that evening.

"Hey Ann, what are you wearing tonight?"

"Mom and I went to Pontiac Mall earlier today, and I got a really cool jean jacket. So I am trying to decide between a white and blue striped shirt that I picked up today or my old faithful Bob Seger concert shirt. What about you?"

"I'm not sure on my top yet either, but jeans for sure. It is still too cold for shorts."

I was about to ask her if Billy was going to drive his parents' Firebird, but before I could get the question out Linda answered it.

"Billy said Wayne is driving, and he wants to leave at seven thirty to get a good parking spot. What a surprise. He's such a control freak!"

*Control freak is right.*

"Well, I better hustle it up then. See you soon."

I placed the receiver back on the base, placed the unit back on the hallway credenza, and took the stairs two at a time to go get ready.

Horror films weren't my thing, but I was looking forward to hanging around outdoors at the drive-in with Linda and Billy. It had been a long, cold winter and a crappy spring. The weather was finally getting nice. The drive-in theatre charged a per car fee, so it was to our benefit to cram in as many friends as possible inside one car. But there were just the four of us that night.

"Five bucks, buddy," Wayne said looking over his shoulder at Billy.

"Screw you man. I bought the beer," Billy replied.

Wayne pulled up to the ticket booth, put the car in park, and pulled his wallet out of his back pocket. He pulled out a ten spot and handed it to the old man. Wayne pulled forward and headed toward the middle of the parking lot. He pulled up next to a speaker pole and put his foot on the brake.

"This good?" he asked, not to any one in particular.

*Not that you care what any of us think.* "Fine," I answered.

While the boys got the cooler and lawn chairs out of the trunk, Linda and I got out of the car and headed to the restroom. Linda took a cigarette out of the pack of Salem 100's she was carrying and pulled a Zippo lighter out of her back pocket. She offered me the pack.

"No thanks. Wayne doesn't like it when I smoke."

Linda rolled her eyes. We used the ladies room, got some popcorn at the concession stand, and headed back to the car. The four of us were sitting in lawn chairs drinking beer, eating popcorn, and talking more than actually watching the movie when the shooting happened.

"Did you hear that?" Billy asked.

"I didn't hear anything," I replied.

"Me either," Linda said.

"Hear what?" Wayne asked.

"It sounded like gunshots, man!"

"Gunshots? You've been smoking too much weed," Wayne snickered.

Commotion a few rows of cars over caught our attention. We heard police sirens in the distance. The sirens got louder. I could see the flashing lights of two police cruisers approaching the drive-in. The movie was shut down and we left.

The paper reported that a boy from Pontiac was with a group of friends acting all tough at the drive-in that night. The kid and his friends approached a car and asked the man in the driver's seat for a light. The man replied he didn't smoke, nor did he have a light. The boy fired two shots into the car, injuring a man and killing his wife, twenty-eight-year-old Deborah Porcelli. Coincidently, they were from Clarkston.[4] But as I said, I don't believe in coincidences.

A week after the shooting at the drive-in, a private airplane crash claimed the lives of three members of a Clarkston family, Mr. Dobson and his two children.[5] The three funerals were held at Billy's dad's funeral home. The family was buried at Lakeview cemetery. Grandma made pies.

As if the deaths of Deborah Porcelli and the Dobson family weren't enough for our town to grieve over that spring, eighteen-month-old Jason Coleman drown on a Friday afternoon after falling into an open septic tank behind his home on Eston Road.[6] The Coleman's lived spitting distance from Grandma. My grandma was devastated.

We all have our routines. Grandma's routine was to stop by our house on Sundays after attending ten o'clock Mass. When asked if she would like anything to drink, she would respond, "a cup of coffee if it isn't too much trouble." Why my mother didn't anticipate the request at approximately eleven o'clock every Sunday and have a fresh pot of coffee ready was beyond me.

I heard the backdoor open and shut. Without looking up from my studies at the kitchen table I greeted her.

"Hi, Grandma. How was church?"

"Hello, Annie. It would have been much nicer had you been there."

Grandma took off her coat. I got up from my chair and walked over, giving her a big hug and a kiss on the cheek. Then I took her coat.

"I just might surprise you one day. Be sitting right up there in the front pew."

"That would be very nice dear. Where is your mother?"

"Seriously, Grandma? Are you new?" I rolled my eyes.

Grandma laughed.

"She should just move out to that barn."

I laughed.

"I agree with you Grandma."

"I just can't shake the death of that baby from my mind." She continued.

"How are the Coleman's doing? Have you seen them?" I asked.

"No, I haven't. So awful to lose a baby. Brings back memories of when your mother lost Eric.  Remember Annie, it's not the things that happen to us that causes us pain, but rather our reaction to them. Everything that happens is all part of God's plan. We just have to remember that. Although it's tough sometimes."


I so admired my grandmother's strength. She wasn't afraid of swimming, driving, biking, or loving. She worried I would struggle with balancing rationality on one hand and the recognition of irrationality on the other. She always told me I was stronger than I gave myself credit for. In just a few weeks I would understand what she meant. I reached deep down and found my strength, and that balance, on a Saturday morning in a car with Wayne.

It was late summer of 1979. Grandma had co-signed a loan for me so I could buy my very first car. Aunt Marty offered to sell me her 1977 Oldsmobile Cutlass Supreme for twelve hundred dollars. I hadn't told anyone outside my family that I was getting a car: not my friends, not even Wayne. I had been working part time at odd jobs and babysitting and had saved just enough money for the down payment. It was so sweet of my aunt to give me such a great deal, a deal I could actually afford.

Grandma took me to the credit union to sign the papers and pick up the cashier's check I needed to pay for the car. Mom drove me to my aunt's house to pick up the car. We traveled the sixty-seven miles from Clarkston to Laingsburg in just under an hour, making small talk along the route. Mom pulled into my aunt's driveway and there she was, my first car: a two-door, baby blue, Cutlass Supreme. Aunt Marty came out of the house, keys in hand. I ran up to her and gave her a big hug. She handed me the keys. I handed her the certified check. I tried to seem interested as she pointed out the car's features and showed me where to find the registration and insurance.

"Would you like to stay and have lunch with your mother and me? I made some sloppy joes."

As tempting as her sloppy joes were, I was too excited to drive my new car to hang around for lunch. So, I thanked her again, hopped in the car, adjusted the seat and the mirrors, and backed out of the driveway.

The car drove smoothly over the country roads as I headed back toward home. I had the car windows down and the radio up. I was on cloud nine. I was the proud owner of my first car. Wayne's car was in the driveway when I arrived. Dad's car was there too. *Dad must be working on the tractor again.* I parked my new car in the driveway and went in the house. Wayne and Dad were visiting at the kitchen table.

"Do you like it?" Dad asked.

"Love it! Come out and see!"

"So, you got a car?" Wayne asked.

"Yes, I did!" I was beaming.

"Come and see!" I grabbed his arm and pulled him up from the kitchen chair.

The three of us went outside.

"That's a fine car, young lady."

"Thanks, Dad!"

Wayne walked around the car, checking it out. He seemed genuinely happy for me and asked me to take him for a ride. We weren't even out of the driveway when trouble started.

"Why didn't you tell me you were buying a car?"

"I wanted to surprise everyone. It's my first car!" I was still beaming.

I carefully turned right out of our driveway onto Allen road. I had only driven a few hundred yards when I felt the blow. Wayne's fist hit me hard in my right ear. The pain was excruciating. I almost passed out. I would later learn the force of his blow ruptured my eardrum. I somehow managed to keep the car going straight down the dirt road as I tried to process what had just happened. Before I could shake off the first blow, he dealt me a second. His left fist backhanded me right across the front of my face. My glasses flew off. My nose started to bleed.

Something came over me. My skin was suddenly hot, as if burning from an extreme fever. Then I got chills and the hair on my arms stood up. I reached deep down and found my strength, and that balance that Grandma told me was inside of me. I slammed on the brake and shifted the car into park. I parked my new car right there in the middle of Allen Road. I released my seatbelt and turned toward Wayne. I launched from my seat and attacked. I started pounding his face with my fists. I screamed, cried, and attacked with every survival instinct I had in me. I was a caged animal unleashed. Wayne was so shocked that he opened his car door and stumbled out onto the road. I reached over and slammed his passenger door shut. I put the car in drive and took off, leaving him there on the side of the road. I drove to the safety of Sue's house. I haven't seen him since. I am no longer afraid. I will never again be a victim. I am a warrior.

High school hadn't been a pleasant experience for me, but I would soon be set free. My last semester was ending in just few days. I hadn't been popular. I didn't belong to any sports teams or clubs. I had endured an abusive, controlling boyfriend. My parents were going through a divorce, and my brother was a drug addict. Yeah, high school was not the best chapter in my life's book. I put my high school memories in a file folder and slammed that drawer. Thank the Lord I had obtained the credits I needed to graduate early, in January, so I could escape the high school institution. I landed a full time office job, leased an apartment, and enrolled in night classes at the local community college. I was ready to launch.

# Twenty
# Freitag Family Tragedy

The year was 1982 and high school was in my rear-view mirror. I was living on my own, working full time and going to night school. I spent Sunday afternoons at Mom's, bumming a decent meal and doing laundry. Per usual, I made my stop at Rudy's Market to pick up some flowers or a fresh baguette for my mother before heading out to the farm.

"Good morning, Doreen." I smiled and waved as I entered Rudy's.

"Good morning Ann. How are you this fine day?" Doreen responded with a smile and a wave.

Doreen is one of seven children born to James and Patricia Freitag. The names of the seven Freitag kids all started with the letter 'D'. There was Debbie, Diane, Denise, Danny, Doreen, Doris, and Darlene. The older kids had dark hair, the three youngest red. All seven had light brown, almost hazel eyes.

Mr. Freitag worked for NCR. He traveled frequently around the Midwest repairing cash registers at grocery stores. Mr. Freitag was one of the first Gerber babies. An honest to goodness real Gerber baby—Mrs. Freitag had pictures. There was no mistaking when Doreen's dad was in the house, he was a big guy with a big voice. Doreen's parents, like mine, fought a lot. I imagine raising seven kids is hard on a marriage. Doreen says they fought about sex a lot. Her mom, a devout Catholic, wouldn't use birth control, and seven kids were enough. The Freitag's lived in a modest home with only one bathroom for nine people.

Mrs. Freitag worked nights as a waitress at the Tally Ho restaurant. She often brought home donuts that hadn't sold by the end of her shift. Sometimes Doreen would bring those donuts to catechism. They were the best darn donuts I've ever had. Mrs. Freitag always had something good cooking on the stove and soft music playing on the kitchen radio. She was a beautiful woman. She sure loved her seven children. One time Doreen jumped off the shed roof and broke her arm. Mrs. Freitag, afraid for Doreen's punishment, lied to her husband about how Doreen got that broken arm.

Debbie joined the army when she was eighteen and never looked back. Diane was the trouble maker of the bunch. She made a sport out of defying her parents. She'd run away from home, four or five days at a time. She always seemed to be in trouble. But oddly, she was Mrs. Freitag's favorite. Diane got pregnant when she was in high school. Diane and her high school sweetheart, Bob, married. Their love child, Bobby, was born in 1976.

Although a bit of a scandalous surprise, the entire Freitag clan supported Diane and Bob and were truly happy and excited about that baby. Bobby was born in September. We had just started tenth grade when Doreen was called down to the office over the PA system and told she was an aunt.

A baby girl, Jennifer, followed the birth of Bobby just a year later. Sadly, Jennifer died as a result of choking on a hot dog at just nine months of age. Her death was ruled accidental at the time.

Jennifer died on August 9, 1980. Police suspected the baby's death may not have been an accident, but they had no proof.

Sadly, police were called to the home of Diane and Bob just two years after Jennifer's death. Their son Bobby, now a kindergartener, failed to show up for school. Bobby was later found dead in the woods near his bus stop. He never got on the school bus. Bobby died on October 25, 1982.[1] Both children are buried at Lakeview Cemetery.

Detectives were certain that Diane had a hand in the deaths of her two children. After Bobby died, the policed exhumed Jennifer's body hoping to find evidence to tie Diane to the baby's death. But none was found. The police never gave up. Finally, after ten years of police pressure, Diane confessed to the murders of her two children.

The tragedy rocked the family to its core, destroyed it really. None of the Freitags would ever be the same. Doreen frequently took her mom to visit Diane in prison and put money into her prison spending account. Diane's trial lasted two weeks. Doreen went every day. Mr. Freitag did not attend. Mr. and Mrs. Freitag moved away. Mrs. Freitag kept every article from the local papers about Diane's case. When she passed away, Doreen found the articles in her mom's closet. Doreen threw all the articles in a box and gave the box to Diane.[2]

I headed toward the checkout, noticing two women whispering and looking in Doreen's direction. I pretended I needed something off the shelf near where they were standing. The two women were gossiping about the family's tragic heartbreak. Through all the press coverage and town gossip surrounding her sister's murder investigation, Doreen held her head high working in that market. She is one of the strongest people I know.

I waited in line to purchase the fresh baguette I had picked up for Mom. The two gossiping women got in line behind me. When it was my turn to check out, I went out of my way to be friendly and chatty with Doreen. I turned and gave the ladies a scolding look as I left the store.

# Twenty-one
# Dairy of a Robbery

With a full stomach and a laundry basket full of clean clothes, I left Mom's and headed back to my apartment. The phone was ringing as I unlocked the door. I ran to grab it before the person on the other line hung up.

"Hello?"

"Hi, Annie. It's your grandmother."

I laughed to myself. *It wasn't like I wouldn't know who she was if she didn't announce herself.*

"Hey, Grandma! What a nice surprise! To what do I owe the pleasure?"

"I have a favor to ask of you."

"Anything, Grandma. What is it?"

"You may find this a bit strange, but would you mind coming out to the lake and spending the night with me tonight?"

"Is everything okay?"

"Well yes, it's just that we had a robbery here at the dairy, and I am a bit shaken up about it is all." I had never known Grandma to be afraid of anything. She felt God kept her safe. So, for her to admit she was scared meant she was really scared.

"I would love to come and spend the night, Grandma. I'll stop on my way and rent a movie and be over in an hour or so."

We said our goodbyes, and I hung up the telephone. I remember the movie I rented that night. It was *Back to the Future.* Grandma loved it.

Richardson Farm Dairy was located at the corner of Clarkston Orion and Eston Roads, right at the end of Grandma's street. The store had a huge statue of a dairy cow in the parking lot. And at one time the statue had a sign on its neck: *Ruthie.* Grandma hated that cow, and she really hated that sign. Can't say I blame her, seeing her name was Ruth. When I was a young girl, she and I would walk to the dairy to get an ice cream treat. Grandma would give the owner the dickens every time we went in that store about the fact that she and Ruthie the cow shared the same name. Eventually the owner got tired of Grandma's nagging, so he took the sign off the cow's neck. But the statue remained for decades.

I poured Grandma and myself a glass of port. "Here you go, Ruthie," I teased as I handed her the glass of wine. I plopped down next to her on the couch and pulled out one of her afghans from a basket on the floor.

"Your mother tells me the company you work for wants you to relocate to Florida." Grandma took a sip of her wine. "Are you considering it, dear?"

"I am considering it, Grandma. I just feel I need to get out of Clarkston for a while. I love it here. It's my home, but I think it is time I see a bit more of the world. My college credits will transfer to Florida Atlantic University so I can still continue my studies."

Grandma and I had a special relationship. We had that special kind of comfortable where we could just be together without feeling the need to say anything. Like Nancy and I did. After a while, I asked her what had her so spooked.

"Francis was shot and killed." she answered solemnly.[1]

"What? When? Where?"

"Last night."

Grandma took another sip of her wine and continued.

"Three men with guns robbed the store. They shot and killed Francis. They shot Charmaine too, but she had a gun behind the counter. She is a tough cookie. Even after she was hit, she was still able to grab her gun and shoot one of the robbers. Your grandfather would have been very proud of her."

"Oh, Grandma, that is awful! I am so sorry. I know how fond you were of Francis."

Grandma turned and looked at me.

"I can't believe I am saying this, but I am beginning to think your curse theory may not be so crazy after all."

We sat silently, drinking our wine. Grandma was the first to break our silence.

"I think you should take the job in Florida, sweetheart. As much as I will miss you, you're young and need to go see the world and have fun."

I didn't answer. I just sat on that old couch, next to my grandmother, both of us looking out at the lake.

"Ready for a movie?"

"You bet."


The paper reported that three armed robbers entered the dairy store wearing ski masks.[2] Charmaine Klaus, the night manager, shot during the robbery, still managed to shoot one of the robbers, a twenty-one-year-old boy from Pontiac, in the face. Surprisingly, the shot didn't kill him. The boy fled through the back door of the store leaving a trail of blood. The police brought in tracking dogs, but the dogs lost the scent. The cashier of the store, Francis Ramsey, just twenty-one, was dead. The following morning a police helicopter scanned the area. Police combed nearby neighborhoods to alert residents to be on the lookout for a wounded suspect. The fact that the armed robber was still on the loose was what had Grandma spooked. The shooter's friends, also suspects, eventually took the wounded boy to Detroit General Hospital where he was apprehended.

There was another article in the paper that caught my eye, just a few pages after the article about the robbery. Charles Raymer lived on Waldon Road with his dad. His dad stabbed him to death. The paper reported there was no motive for the killing.[3]

My decision was made. I was going to accept the job and take the opportunity to move to Florida. But before I could leave, I felt compelled to do something to try to rid the town of its evil. I needed to do something to give me peace that my family and friends would be safe. If anyone could understand my crazy idea, it would be Sue. She was the only friend I had who, like me, truly believed in the power of prayer. Sue wasn't Catholic. She was Lutheran, which was just as good as Catholic as far as I was concerned. God doesn't care what religion you are, just as long as you believe. He doesn't care what church you go to either, just as long as you show up.

Sue and I were chatting on the telephone on a Friday night after a long week of work.

"When are you leaving?"

"My boss wants me down there the first of next month."

"We have to have a party for you, girl."

"That would be nice. But there is something else I need more than a party."

"Sure. Whatcha need?"

"I need you to help me rid Clarkson of this curse. Finally, after all those years of research, I have a plan."

"Are you serious? It's been years since I have thought about The Curse."

"I am very serious. I just don't feel right taking the transfer to Florida unless I'm at peace that I tried to keep you and my family safe. Will you help me?"

"What's your plan?" Sue asked.

"Too many details to explain right now. Next Saturday there's a full moon, so it has to be next Saturday. Your shift ends at ten o'clock, right?"

"Yep, my shift ends at ten. Pick me up about a quarter after and I'll help you."

Sue and I chatted about this and that and then said our good-byes. I hung up the telephone and started making my list. To this day, I cannot function without a list.

I spent the following week mentally and spiritually preparing. I had completed years of research on curses, but I was still a bit unsure of myself. I sought Grandma's councel.

"Would you like some more tea, dear?" Grandma asked as she poured herself another glass of her fabulous sun tea. Grandma smiled at me. Her light blue eyes sparkled.

"In order to battle evil, you have to be filled with the power of the Holy Spirit. You have to ask for God's forgiveness for everything you've done wrong in your life, even the things you cannot remember."

"I haven't been exactly faithful about going to church, Grandma. That concerns me."

"Don't worry about that. Remember, you've been baptized, so God will protect you."

Grandma stood up and went over to her small brown hutch. She opened the door and pulled out an old Bible and a small, very delicate crucifix.

"Take these with you, dear. They will keep you safe."

I left Grandma's and stopped by the local hardware store. Having gathered all the items on my list, I headed back to my apartment. I watched television until late into the night. Sleep eluded me. I tossed and turned until morning. Saturday seemed to drag on and on until it was time for me to pick Sue up. I had spent the day reviewing the plan in my head what seemed to be a hundred times. At nine o'clock in the evening, I took off. I parked my car near the employee entrance and waited for Sue to come out.

"What's the plan?" Sue asked, slamming the passenger car door shut behind her.

"I have all the things we need that are supposed to break The Curse along with some additional things just for good measure. We're heading out to Deer Lake beach, but we have to wait until the full moon, so let's stop by the party store and pick up a six pack."

I handed Sue a five-dollar bill, and she hopped out of the car. She came out of the store a few minutes later with a six pack of Stroh's and an admirer.

"You ladies wanna party?" he asked smiling at Sue as she opened the car door.

"No, sorry man, we are actually going to a funeral. Thanks for the invite though." Sue smiled through the open passenger car window as I started the car.

The young man smiled. "Maybe next time, ladies."

I pulled out onto Andersonville Road and headed toward downtown Clarkston.

"Going to a funeral?" I asked.

"Whatever," Sue said laughing.

I parked the car in the beach parking lot facing the water. Sue and I each popped the top on a cold Stroh's and took a sip. We sat there for an hour or so watching the sunset. When the moon came

198

out, it was time. I grabbed my bag and a small shovel. I tossed Sue the horse blanket out of the back seat.

"Let's go get this done," I said.

We got out of the car, kicked off our shoes, and rolled up the bottoms of our jeans. I circled around the back of the car and popped the trunk to grab a bag of charcoal. We stepped into the shallow water and skirted around the fence. We headed toward a secluded spot on the beach.

We stretched out the horse blanket on the warm sand and sat down. I emptied the contents of my bag. The first item I reached for was holy water. I sprinkled it around our blanket. I pulled the crucifix over my head and placed it around my neck. Sue picked up the sage.

"What's the sage for?"

"My great grandmother used to take a bunch of sage, light it, and let it smolder. She would stand in the middle of her house holding the smoldering sage toward the ceiling and slowly circle it counterclockwise. My great grandmother said it purified the house and made the evil spirits leave." I handed Sue the lighter. She lit the sage and circled it counterclockwise above our heads.

"Should I pray?" asked Sue.

"It certainly can't hurt."

While Sue circled the smoldering sage in the air above our blanket, she led us in prayer.

Then I opened the folded piece of paper I had used to write down the directions and handed Sue a flashlight. She turned it on and shined its beam on the paper I was holding.

"Okay, we are supposed to find a piece of land where nothing grows. That is why I chose the beach. We need to dig a hole twelve inches deep and wide and fill it with charcoal."

"Got it," Sue said grabbing the shovel.

Sue dug the hole while I continued to read.

"It says we are to fill the hole with the charcoal, then find a piece of land where there is green grass near a tree or bush."

Sue momentarily stopped digging, looked around, and pointed. "Over there!"

"Perfect. Then we have to place a white candle in the green grass. I already engraved the name of the devil, *Drevida*, on the bottom of the black candle. We are supposed to light the white candle first and then the black candle. With both candles lit we hold hands and say *Creo del macres ete prestwer.*"

"Okay, then what?"

"Then we extinguish both candles, bury the black candle with the charcoal and the white candle in the ground next to the tree. The Curse is supposed to be gone within seven days."

"Okay, do you think this hole is big enough?" Sue asked, sticking the shovel into a standing position in the soft sand.

"Looks good to me."

While I filled the first hole with charcoal, Sue dug the second hole by the tree. Grabbing the candles and lighter, I joined her at a small grassy spot right near a small birch tree. We lit the white candle first and then the black, just like the directions read. With both candles lit, holding hands, I held the paper so she could see the words with the glow from the full moon. We exchanged a glance and both read the words *Creo del macres ete prestwer.* I then blew out the candles.

"Bury this one with the charcoal," I said, handing Sue the black candle.

I placed the white candle inside the second hole and pushed dirt over it. Having buried the black candle, Sue walked back over to where I was standing.

"Is that it?"

"One more thing, just to be safe."

I reached down on the blanket and grabbed a rabbit's foot

charm. I held it over my heart and said, "With rabbit's foot and magic verse, I turn around this wicked curse. As these words of mine are spoken, let this evil spell be broken."

I turned to Sue, "Now we're done. Let's get out of here before the cops show up."

"What does that saying we said mean anyway?"

I smiled, "I do not believe in your power."

Sue was silent for a moment and then she smiled at me.

"Well I believe in yours, Ann Johns."

I laughed.

# Epilogue

I have no idea if Sue and I broke the curse that night or not. What I do know is that now, more than thirty years later, the rash of deaths in our small down seems to have ceased. However, with that being said, many old time Clarkston residents believe our town is haunted: some believe by the spirit of Enos Church.[1,2]

Enos Church was born in 1813. He served as Clarkston's Township Supervisor, Town Clerk, and Justice of the Peace in the 1800s. Enos was also the Master of the Masonic Temple. No one really knows why Enos haunts our small town, but both the Masonic Temple and Enos' former residence in downtown Clarkston are supposedly haunted.

Enos's former residence is now the home of the current Clarkston city manager. She has reported the front door opens on its own even when it is locked. Members of the Masonic Temple have stated they have felt Enos' presence and have even seen the spirit of a man in a long coat entering the building through its brick exterior.

According to the Clarkston Community Historical Society, the Masonic Temple is one of the most active hauntings in town. It has been reported that the Mason's ceremonial bell chime goes off on its own, the lobby light fixture flickers off and on, strange orbs appear in photographs, and a person's shadow has been seen melting into the walls. I sincerely do not believe that the spirit of Enos Church was in any way connected to the tragedies that occurred while I was growing up, but perhaps something paranormal was a contributing factor.

I returned to Clarkston in 2002 and have settled back in. Sue still lives in the area, and we see each other often. Mom retired to Florida where the weather is more conducive to riding horses every day of the year. Dad, a WWII vet, passed away on Memorial Day, May 30, 2016. He was 91. Patrick still lives locally. Every day is a struggle.

My friend Billy attended Western Michigan University, and took over stewardship of the funeral home when his father passed away in 1992. Diane confessed to the murder of her two children and was released from prison after serving a fifteen-year sentence. Doreen started her own small cleaning and catering business. She takes care of many Clarkston families, including mine. Steve Howe's family started the Howe's Scholarship, which is awarded every year to Clarkston varsity baseball and softball players in his memory.

I still run into Mrs. Powe around town now and again. She is still just as sweet as she always was. Dad ran into Mr. Powe at a local diner just a few months before he died. The two men shared a few stories and had a few laughs over "them damn cows."

I learned a hard lesson growing up in a small town plagued by tragedy. I learned that bad things can and do happen, not just to other people; they can happen to us and the people we love. My childhood forced me to see how brutal our world can be and how fragile our lives are. As I live on, others continue to die, and I and the others who love them will be left behind to pick up the pieces of our lives. I have learned not to let the meanness of others or the evil in the world touch the beauty of my human spirit. I have learned that I can overcome almost anything.

# Notes

## Chapter 2 Don't Play with Guns

1 November 27, 1969 "Clarkston saddened by the death of John", by Jean Sura
2 November 27, 1969 "Plane crash claims 3 lives"
3 November 14, 1968 "Boy killed by empty gun"

## Chapter 4 Tornado of a Move

1 Detroit riots
   https://en.wikipedia.org/wiki/1967_Detroit_riot
2 Detroit riots
   http://www.detroits-great-rebellion.com/
3 1952 tornado
   http://www.geostat.org/data/berkley-mi/tornados
4 October 3, 1968 "Another Day" by Constance Lektzian "The Allen Family"

## Chapter 5 Night Terrors

1 June 4, 1970 "Boy killed on way to school"
2 August 27, 1970 "Doyle arraignment set September 8"
3 July 30, 1970 "Kidnapping suspect held for trial exam"

## Chapter 6 Allen Road

1 Ellis Barn
http://lakeorionreview.com/historic-ellis-barn-begins-move-to-new-home/

2 July 7, 1977 "Horse history of Michigan to be relived by club's anniversary" by Jean Saile

3 March 19, 1970 "Hold boy, 16, in brutal killing of township man"

4 June 27, 1968 "Grinding crash kills 3 area teen-agers"

5 July 25, 1968 "Swimming accident injures local youth"

6 July 30, 1970 "Jack slips injures man"

7 August 15, 1968 "Drive shaft injures youth"

8 August 1, 1968, Obituaries, Gerald Frich

9 June 19, 1969 "Youth drowns in gravel pit"

## Chapter 7 Emergency Room Visit

1 August 13, 1970 "Tot drowns in Townsend Lake"

## Chapter 9 Lost

1 February 18, 1971 "Train-car crash injures three"

2 March 4, 1971 "Accident kills local man"

3 May 20, 1971 "Construction worker crushed in accident"

4 May 27, 1971 "CHS sophomore drowns in Gulick Lake"

5 July 29, 1971 "Death seals mystery" by Jean Sura

## Chapter 10 Seabiscuit

1 Michigan State Fairgrounds
https://michiganstatefairllc.wordpress.com/general-information/archives/

2 The Governor's Handicap Race
http://www.thedec.us/statefairclosing.htm

3 July 11, 1974 "State fair time"

4 Jackson 5 at the State Fair

http://michaeljackson.wikia.com/wiki/The_Jackson
_5_US_Tour

5 October 12, 1972 "Marijuana raid nets 640 pounds"

6 March 2, 1972 "Village 'hot bed' for drug traffic", by Jean Saile

7 April 27, 1972 "Killed in crash"

8 July 27, 1972 "Eric Booth, drowning victim"

9 January 11, 1973 "Mother arrested for sons' murders"

10 August 16, 1973 "Warrant sought in auto death"

11 March 29, 1973 "Manslaughter charged in auto game deaths"

12 March 22, 1973 "Two die in crash"

13 August 8, 1974 "Bike accident victim satisfactory"

14 June 6, 1968 "Another day" by Constance Lektzian "Sam Miller pioneer child"

15 July 18, 1968 "The Sam Miller Farm Centennial Living" by Constance Lektzian

16 July 2, 1970 "Killed in farm accident" by Constance Lektzian

## Chapter 11 Death to Deer Lake

1 Deer Lake and Clinton River
https://en.wikipedia.org/wiki/Clinton_River_(Michigan)

2 June 5, 1975 "Snakes alive! They're rattling in Clarkston" by Mary Warner

3 June 12, 1975 "Snake capital of Michigan"

4 May 15, 1969 "Massasauga Rattler strikes again" by Jean Sura

5 Clarkston population
http://www.indetwp.com/residents/township_profile/index.php

6 July 18, 1974 "Close call on lake", Dear Editor, Mrs. Frob Gruenberg

7 Native American burial grounds, Dixie Highway
https://en.wikipedia.org/wiki/U.S._Route_24_in_Michigan

8 Rouge River burial grounds

http://anthropology.msu.edu/anp264-ss15/2015/03/03/
moundbuilders-in-michigan/
9  August 1, 1974 "Northview slaying puzzles police", by Jean Saile
10 November 14, 1974 "Youth drowns in Whipple Lake boat mishap"
11 Nov 21, 1974 "Death controversy hits Clarkston"
12 January 2, 1975 "Long-time resident killed by car"
13 January 16, 1975 "Springfield man charged in auto death"
14 February 20, 1975 "Girl killed by auto on Sashabaw"
15 February 27, 1975 "Boy succumbs to snowmobile injuries"
16 June 17, 1971 "Bicycle-car crash injures boy 7"
17 Agust 16, 1962 "Coach Drowns in Deer Lake

## Chapter 12 Tragedy Hits the Slopes
1  February 27, 1975 "Man falls to death from Pine Knob lift"
2  April 24, 1975 "One dead, 3 injured in traffic"
3  July 10, 1975 "Husband arraigned on charges he shot wife"
4  May 19, 1977 "It was the last roundup, Destry (Dick Powe) won't
   ride again" Jean Saile
5  December 16, 1971 "Tina Smith hurt on Dixie"
6  July 5, 1973 "Two youth injured in bike collision"

## Chapter 13 Tragedy Strikes Again
1  September 13, 1973 "Mother of four killed in auto accident"
2  September 20, 1973 "Accident claims second victim"
3  September 20, 1973 "Bicyclist, 14, killed in collision"
4  October 25, 1973 "Girl becomes second accident victim"
5  April 11, 1974 "Two Maceday youths drown"
6  May 16, 1974 "Girl recovering from freak school mishap"
7  June 27, 1974 "Boy killed in gun mishap"
8  July 11, 1974 "State fair time"
9  October 25, 1973 "Two township men killed in weekend
accidents"

## Chapter 14 The Clarkston Curse

1 October 25, 1973 "Two township men killed in weekend accidents"

2 September 13, 1973 "Two hurt in bus accident"

3 October 11, 1973 "Girl injured alighting from school bus"

4 October 11, 1973, "Woman dies in M-15 crash"

5 January 8, 1976 "Clarkston girl killed in Posen"

6 February 5, 1976 "Local youths charged in Clintonville murder"

7 February 26, 1976 "Clarkston girl slain returning from Florida"

8 August 5, 1976 "Young folk gather for county fair", Country Living, Mary Warner

9 August 5, 1976 "Rock concert at 4-H fair"

10 July 22, 1976 "Clarkston girl safe after near tragedy in Glacier"

11 July 7, 1977 "Murder witness shotgunned"

12 Shadowlands Haunted Places
http://www.theshadowlands.net/places/michigan.htm

13 May 13, 1976 "Accidents kill two, injure more"

14 December 8, 1966 "Another day" by Constance Lektzian

15 Tiger Stadium
http://detroithistorical.org/learn/encyclopedia-of-detroit/corktown-historic-district

16 Robert Fick
https://en.wikipedia.org/wiki/Tiger_Stadium_(Detroit)

17 March 31, 1977 "Boy 11, escapes serious injury"

18 June 10, 1976 "Six year old hurt in freak accident"

19 Steve Howe
http://clarkstonnews.com/champs-remember-glory-years/

20 July 15, 1976 "Freak accident kills girl"

## Chapter 15 Oakland County Child Killer

1 Mark Stebbins
https://en.wikipedia.org/wiki/Oakland_County_Child_Killer

2  Kristine Mihelich
   http://www.wxyz.com/news/local-news/investigations/inves-
   tigators-follow-new-leads-in-30-year-old-murder-case-that-
   haunts-detroit-area

3  Mrs. King letter
   http://greatadthulhu.angelfire.com/page6.html

4, 5  Oakland County Child Killer
   https://en.wikipedia.org/wiki/Oakland_County_Child_Killer
   http://www.leelanaunews.com/news/2014-03-06/Front_
   Page/37_years_No_answers.html

6  June 19, 1975 "Man accused in kidnap attempt"

7  July 31, 1975 "Clarkston youth dies in crash"

8  June 19, 1975 "Girl killed on Dixie"

9  John Kirchgessner
   http://www.apnewsarchive.com/1986/Pilot-Of-One-
   Plane-Involved-In-Mid-Air-Crash-Dies/id-3c1551f95d-
   211636688de072cb715041

## Chapter 16 Fires Burn

1  May 5, 1977 "Morgan's heavily damaged by fire"

2  July 7, 1977 "Drowning averted"

3  Illegal imports
   https://www.fws.gov/news/Historic/NewsReleases/
   1979/19790802.pdf

4  July 7, 1977 "Mrs. Stageman doing well"

5  March 31, 1977 "Boy 11, escapes serious injury"

6  June 16, 1977 "Canadian boy killed here"

7  August 1, 1974 "Northview slaying puzzles police", by Jean Saile

## Chapter 17 Home Town Hero

1  June 14, 1973 "Rudy's Market up for sale" by Jean Saile

2  January 20, 1977 "A guardian for the flock"

3 Blizzard of 1978

https://michpics.wordpress.com/2016/01/26/
remembering-the-michigan-blizzard-of-1978/

4 February 2, 1978 "Disaster averted in '78 storm", Rhea Lodge

5 June 13, 1979 "Steve Howe signs with Dodgers"

6 Steve Howe

http://riveraveblues.com/2012/02/the-tragic-tale-of-
steve-howe-63877/

7 Dodgers beat Yankees

http://www.baseball-reference.com/players/h/howest01.shtml

8 Rookie of the Year

http://riveraveblues.com/2012/02/the-tragic-tale-of-
steve-howe-63877/http://riveraveblues.com/2012/02/
the-tragic-tale-of-steve-howe-63877/

9 Steve Howe drug trouble

http://www.washingtonpost.com/wp-dyn/content/arti-
cle/2006/04/30/AR2006043001054.html

10 Steve Howe retires

https://www.google.com/webhp?sourceid=chrome-
instant&ion=1&espv=2&ie=UTF-8#q=Steve%E2%80%99s+ho
we+baseball+career+ended+with+the+strike+of+1995

11 Steve Howe dies

http://articles.latimes.com/2006/apr/29/local/me-howe29

## Chapter 18 Innocence Shattered

1 May 2, 1979 "I-75 head-on crash kills three Sunday"

2 July 18, 1979 "Police crack down on park partiers"

3 November 14, 1979 "Manslaughter charges brought in accident"

4 August 1, 1979 "Thanks from the Fry family"

## Chapter 19 Death at the Drive-In

1 August 8, 1979 "Fiery crash kills Springfield resident Paul Valentino"

2 September 5, 1979 "Plane crash claims two local men"

3 March 19, 1980 "Second man gets life in Hockey case"

4 May 7, 1980 "Suspect arrested in drive-in murder"

5 May 14, 1980 "Ontario plane crash claims three lives"

6 May 21, 1980 "Independence child drowns"

7 June 27, 1979 "Local drug picture unfocused"

## Chapter 20 Freitag Family Tragedy

1 Bobby death
http://www.theoaklandpress.com/article/OP/20080924/NEWS/309249989

2 Schwarze, D. (2017, February 26). Personal interview.

## Chapter 21 Dairy of a Robbery

1 March 19, 1980 "Three suspects charged with murder"

2 June 25, 1980, Wednesday "Judge delays toothy decision" by Marilyn Trumper

3 June 23, 1980 "Father charged with son's murder"

## Epilogue

1 Haunted Clarkston
http://www.theoaklandpress.com/article/OP/20130815/NEWS/308159830

2 Enos Church
http://clarkstonnews.com/clarkston-haunts-on-halloween/

# References

The following articles from *The Clarkston News* were used to verify that my memories were not the result of an overactive child's imagination, but were, in fact, true:

August 16, 1962 "Coach drowns in Deer Lake"

October 13, 1966 "Area youngsters injured in accidents"

December 8, 1966 "Another day" by Constance Lektzian

August 24, 1967 "Another day" by Constance Lektzian "Indian legends of Independence"

June 6, 1968 "Another day" by Constance Lektzian "Sam Miller pioneer child"

June 27, 1968 "Grinding crash kills 3 area teen-agers"

July 18, 1968 "The Sam Miller Farm Centennial Living" by Constance Lektzian

July 25, 1968 "Swimming accident injures local youth"

August 1, 1968, Obituaries, Gerald Frich

August 15, 1968 "Drive shaft injures youth"

October 3, 1968 "Another Day" by Constance Lektzian "The Allen Family"

November 14, 1968 "Boy killed by empty gun"

May 15, 1969 "Massasauga Rattler strikes again" by Jean Sura

June 19, 1969 "Youth drowns in gravel pit"November 27, 1969 "Plane crash claims 3 lives"

November 27, 1969 "Clarkston saddened by the death of John", by Jean Sura

March 12, 1970 "Collision kills 8 year old"

March 19, 1970 "Hold boy, 16, in brutal killing of township man"

June 4, 1970 "Boy killed on way to school"

July 2, 1970 "Killed in farm accident" by Constance Lektzian

July 30, 1970 "Kidnapping suspect held for trial exam"

July 30, 1970 "Jack slips injures man"

August 13, 1970 "Tot drowns in Townsend Lake"

August 27, 1970 "Doyle arraignment set September 8"

February 18, 1971 "Train-car crash injures three"

March 4, 1971 "Accident kills local man"

May 20, 1971 "Construction worker crushed in accident"

May 27, 1971 "CHS sophomore drowns in Gulick Lake"

June 17, 1971 "Bicycle-car crash injures boy 7"

July 29, 1971 "Death seals mystery" by Jean SuraDecember 16, 1971 "Tina Smith hurt on Dixie"

March 2, 1972 "Village 'hot bed' for drug traffic", by Jean Saile

April 27, 1972 "Killed in crash"

July 27, 1972 "Eric Booth, drowning victim"

October 12, 1972 "Marijuana raid nets 640 pounds"

January 11, 1973 "Mother arrested for sons' murder"

March 22, 1973 "Two die in crash"

March 29, 1973 "Manslaughter charged in auto game deaths"

June 14, 1973 "Rudy's Market up for sale" by Jean Saile

July 5, 1973 "Two youth injured in bike collision"

August 16, 1973 "Warrant sought in auto death"

September 13, 1973 "Mother of four killed in auto accident"

September 13, 1973 "Two hurt in bus accident"

September 20, 1973 "Accident claims second victim"

September 20, 1973 "Bicyclist, 14, killed in collision"

October 11, 1973 "Girl injured alighting from school bus"

October 11, 1973, "Woman dies in M-15 crash"

October 25, 1973 "Girl becomes second accident victim"

October 25, 1973 "Two township men killed in weekend accidents"

April 11, 1974 "Two Maceday youths drown"

May 16, 1974 "Girl recovering from freak school mishap"

July 11, 1974 "State fair time"

June 27, 1974 "Boy killed in gun mishap"

July 18, 1974 "Close call on lake", Dear Editor, Mrs. Frob Gruenberg

August 1, 1974 "Northview slaying puzzles police", by Jean Saile

August 1, 1974 "Six year old girl traffic fatality"

August 8, 1974 "Bike accident victim satisfactory"

November 14, 1974 "Youth drowns in Whipple Lake boat mishap"

Nov 21, 1974 "Death controversy hits Clarkston"

January 2, 1975 "Long-time resident killed by car"

January 16, 1975 "Springfield man charged in auto death"

February 27, 1975 "Man falls to death from Pine Knob lift"

February 27, 1975 "Boy succumbs to snowmobile injuries"

February 20, 1975 "Girl killed by auto on Sashabaw"

April 24, 1975 "One dead, 3 injured in traffic"

June 5, 1975 "Snakes alive! They're rattling in Clarkston" Mary Warner

June 12, 1975 "Snake capital of Michigan"

June 19, 1975 "Man accused in kidnap attempt"

June 19, 1975 "Girl killed on Dixie"

July 10, 1975 "Husband arraigned on charges he shot wife"

July 31, 1975 "Clarkston youth dies in crash"

January 8, 1976 "Clarkston girl killed in Posen"

February 26, 1976 "Clarkston girl slain returning from Florida"

February 5, 1976 "Local youths charged in Clintonville murder"

May 13, 1976 "Accidents kill two, injure more"

June 10, 1976 "Six year old hurt in freak accident"

July 22, 1976 "Clarkston girl safe after near tragedy in Glacier"

July 15, 1976 "Freak accident kills girl"

August 5, 1976 "Rock concert at 4-H fair"

August 5, 1976 "Young folk gather for county fair", Country Living, Mary Warner

January 20, 1977 "A guardian for the flock"

May 5, 1977 "Morgan's heavily damaged by fire"

May 19, 1977 "It was the last roundup, Destry (Dick Powe) won't ride again" Jean Saile

March 31, 1977 "Boy 11, escapes serious injury"

June 16, 1977 "Canadian boy killed here"

July 7, 1977 "Drowning averted"

July 7, 1977 "Mrs. Stageman doing well"

July 7, 1977 "Murder witness shotgunned"

July 7, 1977 "Horse history of Michigan to be relived by club's anniversary" by Jean Saile

February 2, 1978 "Disaster averted in '78 storm", Rhea Lodge

May 2, 1979 "I-75 head-on crash kills three Sunday"

June 13, 1979 "Steve Howe signs with Dodgers"

June 27, 1979 "Local drug picture unfocused"

July 18, 1979 "Police crack down on park partiers"August 1, 1979 "Thanks from the Fry family"

August 8, 1979 "Fiery crash kills Springfield resident Paul Valentino"

September 5, 1979 "Plane crash claims two local men"

November 14, 1979 "Manslaughter charges brought in accident"

March 19, 1980 "Three suspects charged with murder"

March 19, 1980 "Second man gets life in Hockey case"

May 7, 1980 "Suspect arrested in drive-in murder"

May 14, 1980 "Ontario plane crash claims three lives"

May 21, 1980 "Independence child drowns"June 23, 1980 "Father charged with son's murder"

June 25, 1980, Wednesday "Judge delays toothy decision" by Marilyn Trumper

Schwarze, D. (2017, February 26). Personal interview.

Ann Johns

Billy Wint

Brenda Robbins

Danny Freitag

Doreen Freitag

Diane Freitag

Joe Fry

J. Abbot

Jack Thompson

Fearnow

Kyle Johnson

M. Jones

Mike Seymour

Michael Claus

Nancy Rekawek

Rob Kuechle

Steve Howe

Susan Plummer

Patricia Tisch

Mr. Kirchgessner

Cindy Pidd and David Kennedy

Clarkston year book photos compliments of Winship Photography

Dear Editor:

As a new resident in Clarkston I am amazed at the seeming lack of concern on the part of many residents over the proposed development at the north end of Deer Lake. The potential effect of the project on the entire community is alarming, to say the least.

The proposed 916 additional residential units and shopping center will obviously generate a great deal of traffic. What will happen to Bluegrass Drive and Holcomb Road when each of these 916 people leave for work every morning? Bluegrass Drive, which is right across the street from one of the proposed entrances to the development, will be a straight shot to I-75 and M-15. Holcomb Road, of course, will be the primary exit to Pontiac and points south. The planning commission itself states that the potential traffic on Holcomb Road will be close to the maximum allowable before the road would have to be widened to four lanes.

How many new schools will have to be built to accomodate these new residents? How much will this cost in additional tax dollars? Or do the people of Clarkston want to keep their present schools and simply increase the size of the classes? Either way we lose.

According to the developmental plan, the sewage from the entire project, including the shopping center and multiples on Dixie Highway, will empty into the Holcomb Road sewer system. How much of the area around Deer Lake will be destroyed to accomplish this feat? If ten percent of these new residents use the lake for boating it will mean 91 additional boats on the lake. How safe will people feel with that much traffic on the water? How enjoyable will it be to fish or swim or simply enjoy the peace and quiet of the lake in the early morning or evening hours.

Finally, what if the proposed project were partially completed and, for one reason or another, was suddenly stopped? Suppose it got tied up in court for months, or years. What kind of eyesores, possibly dangerous eyesores, would be left behind? Do we really need, much less want, such problems?

I believe that the residents of this area should pressure their township officials to do everything possible to defeat the lawsuit which threatens to destroy Deer Lake and bring urban sprawl to Independence Township. I appeal to each of you to make yourself heard on this issue.

Douglas M. Carlson

Letter to editor February 14, 1974

Clarkston Storm
compliments of retroplanet.com

Photos of Rudy Schwarze and Rudy's Market's staff from Clarkston Newspaper
Original caption from bottom photo reads:

Rudy's market is practically a two-family operation, shared by the Schwarzes, the owners and the Freitags, who work there. Because almost all store employees will be in attendance at the wedding, which joins a Schwarze and a Freitag, Rudy's must close. From left are owner Rudy Schwarze, new daughter-in-law Doreen Freitag, Doreen's mom Pat and twin brother Dan, and Rudy's son Bob. Bridegroom Fred is absent from the picture.

Patrick and Annie Johns, 1963

John and Ruth Tisch (Grandma and Grandpa)
on Walters Lake dock, 1957

Clarence Edward (Clancy) Johns
Photo compliments of Kari Natrass

Patricia Kathryn O'Conner (Patsy) Tisch Johns